BRITISH POND LANDSCAPES

ACTION FOR PROTECTION AND ENHANCEMENT

PROCEEDINGS OF THE UK CONFERENCE OF THE POND *Life* PROJECT
HELD AT UNIVERSITY COLLEGE, CHESTER
7TH - 9TH 1997

Edited by John Boothby

The Pond *Life* Project
Liverpool John Moores University
15-21 Webster St.
LIVERPOOL L3 2ET
United Kingdom

Pond Action
School of Biological and Molecular Sciences
Oxford Brookes University, Gipsy lane Campus
Headington, OXFORD, OX3 0BP
United Kingdom

British Library Catalogue-in-Publication Data.
A catalogue record for this book is available from the British Library.

ISBN: 0 9531291 0 1

Published by: The Pond *Life* Project.
Telephone: 0151-231-4044/4046
Fax: 0151-258-1224
email: j.boothby@livjm.ac.uk

Printed in Great Britain by Colin Cross Printers Ltd, Garstang, Lancashire.

EMM
(Boo)

0179174

sm9900S763
4|00
£15-00
AMBRES

S726
(Pon).

1 Week Loan

This book is due for return on or before the last date shown below.

ii

CONTENTS

Theme III: Pond landscape change: habitat and species perspectives

Theme IV: Strategies for protecting ponds and pond landscapes

Poster Papers

Preface

This volume comprises written contributions to the British Pond Landscapes Conference, organised by the Pond *Life* Project in cooperation with Pond Action.

The theme of the Conference, which was held at University College, Chester on the 7th - 9th September 1997, was "towards an appreciation of Britain's pond landscapes and the steps necessary for their conservation". This conference contributes to a growing concern for the conservation of ponds as distinctive landscapes, and was concerned not only with the ecology of ponds, but also with the political, economic, legal, and structural environments within which conservation is, or could be, undertaken. The emphasis is firmly on the British context; a second conference, to be held in Maastricht in 1998, will examine comparisons and contrasts across Northern Europe.

The Conference organisers wish to thank all those who contributed papers and posters to ensure a successful conference, to the sponsors for their financial support, and to the various groups and companies who provided delegate and display material.

John Boothby

September 1997

Theme I:

Wetland landscapes and landscape degradation in the UK

Pond loss and amphibians; historical perspective

R. S. Oldham[1] & M. J. S. Swan[2]

[1]Department of Biological Sciences, De Montfort University, Leicester LE7 9SU, UK
[2]Amphibian Habitat Advisory Services, 19 St. Judith's Lane, Sawtry, Cambs. PE17 5XE, UK

Abstract

Over the period of about one hundred years, data from over 200 surveys in the UK indicate pond loss as high as ninety percent, with corresponding reductions in pond density, to a median of 1.4 ponds km^{-2}. The impact on amphibians is probably even greater than these raw statistics suggest since they do not take account of the fact that about 50% of existing ponds are now unsuitable as habitat. In many surveyed areas the mean inter-pond distance was greater than that required for effective amphibian dispersal. However, the late nineteenth century was the golden age of the pond, numbers greatly enhanced as a result of the Enclosure Acts, and in earlier times ponds were much less common. In pre-Enclosures Britain, with a shortage of breeding sites in many parts of the country, amphibian status was probably determined largely by the carrying capacity of the aquatic habitat. Subsequently, about a century ago, there were relatively few constraints, a high pond density being coupled with diverse terrestrial habitat in agricultural landscapes rich in hedges, ditches, wetland and woodland. Major change began at about the start of the Second World War, especially through agricultural intensification, including land drainage, when there was a reduction in both aquatic and terrestrial carrying capacity, clearly reflected in the results of post-war surveys of amphibian status. Pond numbers continue to be restrictive but in many areas it is the lack of terrestrial habitat diversity that is now the main limiting factor, preventing colonisation and recolonisation of the remaining ponds. On the other hand, in some parts of the country there is now room for guarded optimism, recent surveys suggesting that the status of some species has either stabilised or is improving.

Introduction

In this paper we review existing data on pond loss and consider quantitative and qualitative habitat changes with respect to amphibians. We attempt to put habitat changes into a historical perspective and consider their likely impact on the status of amphibian populations, especially since the Second World War.

Pond loss statistics

Sources of material

A large-scale survey, involving volunteer surveyors, conducted as part of the National Amphibian Survey (Swan and Oldham, 1993: 180 records, involving over 11,500 ponds) combined with a compendium of diverse accounts in the literature (Oldham and Swan, 1995:

68 records, involving over 220,000 ponds) form the basis of the current treatment of pond statistics. The majority (76%) of the surveys, relate exclusively to the post-war period (Figure 1).

Interpretation of trends

The interpretation of published surveys is complicated by the variety of methods used. Surveys using a comparison of maps of different dates, aerial photographs, questionnaires and field work are each subject to different limitations. Maps of differing scales and of uncertain publication dates may be used, there may be differing concepts of what constitutes a pond in terms of size; garden ponds may be included or excluded. The validation methods used in the National Amphibian Survey (Swan and Oldham, 1993) help to avoid some of these difficulties, but again the survey is subject to variation in the perceptions of different surveyors. Despite the difficulties certain trends are indicated.

Changes in pond numbers

The extent of loss in pond numbers relative to gain for 149 non-garden surveys is illustrated in Figure 2. In a high proportion of the surveys there was a net loss of ponds, the median being 33% loss. A typical pattern, with relative stability before the Second World War and dramatic loss during and after it, is illustrated by one of the surveys (Figure 3). The overall trend when the annual percentage changes in pond numbers are plotted relative to dates of survey (Figure 4a), in common with the example in Figure 3, suggests a gradual decline in numbers up to about the Second World War. The greater variability after about 1960 may be partly the result of using a large number of relatively small surveys. However, it probably also indicates a real divergence between some areas in which positive efforts are being made to conserve and create ponds and others in which the pressures of modern agriculture and urban expansion are causing increasing rates of loss. When the data are accumulated into ten year periods (Figure 4b) the most recent trends are encouraging. Our sampling programme was non-random, but an indication that our data provide a reasonable reflection of the overall national picture is suggested by the results of a recent national survey (Barr et al., 1994). This was based upon 384 randomly chosen areas of 1 km^2, surveyed in 1984 and again in 1990. It indicated a loss of between 4 and 9% (0.7 and 1.5% per annum). For comparitive purposes this has been included in Figure 4a. The result indicates a slightly lower loss rate than the corresponding ten-year median value in Figure 4b.

Numerically, garden ponds provide a major source of new ponds. These are difficult to survey, they are usually omitted from published records, and they are excluded from the above summaries, although included in the original data sets. When field ponds are destroyed during urban expansion, subsequent gains in numbers of garden ponds may outweigh the original losses. In one example (Oldham & Swan, 1995) there was a loss of 18 field ponds through urbanisation, but a gain of 35 garden ponds in the same area. Garden ponds commonly occur in much higher density than field ponds. We estimate a density of about 100 garden ponds km^{-2} from data in Banks & Laverick (1986) and Beebee (1979) estimated there were over 200 km^{-2} in the Brighton area. Similar values have been found in other studies (Langton, 1991, Latham et al., 1994). These contrast with the median field pond density of less than 2 km^{-2} in contemporary surveys (see later). However, despite the compensation in numbers, garden ponds are unlikely to make up for field ponds qualitatively in floral and faunal diversity; amongst amphibians the crested newt and the common toad are uncommon in garden ponds.

4

Reasons for pond loss and perceived threats to existing ponds were documented by the National Amphibian Survey and reported by Oldham and Swan (1991). Urban expansion and agricultural developments, including the introduction of piped water and the expansion of arable agriculture, accounted for the majority (74%) of actual losses, but pond senescence, the natural consequence of hydroseral succession, was the most commonly reported threat (32%) to existing ponds. Successional change could well be underestimated because of its gradual nature and the absence of a clearly defined end point.

Ponds as amphibian habitat

Although amphibians use several kinds of water bodies as breeding sites, ponds predominate and other aquatic habitats will be ignored in the current work. Again, although the natterjack toad is included in the amphibian fauna it has a much narrower distribution than the other five species (common frog and toad, smooth, palmate and crested newts) and is distinctive in several ways. It will be largely excluded from the current work.

Pond densities

Pond numbers have little meaning unless related to the area in which they occur. Most (over 60%) of the surveys were undertaken in a measured area and examples of the ranges and central tendencies of the corresponding pond densities from different periods are illustrated in Figure 5. Pond densities, and consequent inter-pond distances, determine the ease with which amphibians can disperse between breeding sites. These have declined dramatically since the Second World War. The median pond density, recorded in surveys between 1982 and 1991, of 1.4 ponds km^{-2} (Figure 5) corresponds to a mean inter-pond distance of 0.85 km.

A geographic trend in pond densities in Britain was noted by Swan & Oldham (1993) with a suggestion of higher densities in lowland England especially in the west and lower densities in Scotland and parts of eastern England.

Qualitative changes in pond habitats

Changes in pond density provide one method of evaluating pond habitat, but clearly not all ponds are equally suitable as breeding sites. There are basic minimum requirements of space, water quality, larval food production and security from predation as well as more specific requirements for the viability of each species. The evaluation of habitat quality presents a much greater problem than the assessment of pond density; two approaches are described.

Hydroseral succession

Beyond a certain degree of encroachment by macrophytes it becomes impossible for amphibians to breed successfully. The National Amphibian Survey (Swan & Oldham, 1993) included an assessment of the degree of macrophyte encroachment in ponds. Beyond 75% encroachment, ponds no longer act as satisfactory breeding sites for most British species. About 18% of the ponds surveyed had encroachment values greater than 75%. If this is characteristic of ponds nationally then the median effective pond density is lower than the 1.4 km^{-2} shown in Figure 5.

Amphibian diversity

The occurrence of amphibians themselves provides an alternative method of assessing pond quality. Since many organisms share basic requirements, this will have meaning beyond the immediate taxonomic group.

Data from 99 blanket surveys (Swan & Oldham, 1993) indicate that the proportion containing breeding populations was 59%, the remainder being unused by any amphibian. Sites were not used because of a combination of unsuitable pond habitat (incorporating reductions due to pond senescence, discussed above) and unsuitable terrestrial habitat. For all species combined this reduces the extrapolated value for the effective pond density to 0.80 ponds km^{-2} and the median inter-pond distance to 1.12 km.

Amphibian dispersion

The National Amphibian Survey data also provide a measure of the extent to which the special requirements of each of the five commoner species are satisfied. Occupancy of ponds, within the areas of distribution of each species, ranged from a median of 17 % for the palmate newt to 47 % for the common frog (Figure 6). Corresponding values for the effective pond densities and inter-pond distances, based upon corrections to the data in Figure 5, are also provided in Figure 6. Limits of the dispersal distance for the British amphibians are not known with any certainty. The common toad and the crested newt are known to move at least 1 km from the breeding site (Reading *et al.*, 1991, Oldham, 1995, Arntzen & Wallis, 1991, Oldham & Swan, 1991); additionally there is evidence for the crested newt (Swan & Oldham, 1993) that occurrence is unlikely in areas where the pond density is less than 0.7 ponds km^{-2} (inter-pond distance 1.2 km). If we take 1 km as the notional dispersal value for all the common species, then 38% of the 132 surveys referred to in Figure 5 have a mean inter-pond distance above this limit. Taking account of the likelihood of occurrence (Figure 6) we have at least 62% of the 132 survey areas with a pond dispersion too sparse to permit dispersal of any of the species (rising to 90% for the palmate and crested newts), assuming the ponds are evenly dispersed. Clearly, however, pond dispersion is not uniform and amphibians may occupy and move between clusters of ponds within areas which otherwise have a sparse pond density.

Wider habitat requirements of amphibians

One of the distinguishing features of ponds is their propensity to disappear during part of the year, usually the summer. Species using them, including amphibians, are usually adapted to survive out of water for part of each year. Indeed all the British amphibian species spend the majority of their lives on land and much of their growth and productivity is accomplished by exploiting terrestrial habitats. An assessment of amphibian status must consider the availability of terrestrial habitat.

Trends in land use

Changes in the availability of terrestrial habitat are much more difficult to document than changes in pond numbers. Precise habitat requirements are not fully understood and even if they were, habitat occurrence is unlikely to be mapped in appropriate terms. If we exclude gardens, the National Amphibian Survey indicated gross amphibian habitat preferences as woodland > rough grassland > improved grassland > arable land (Swan & Oldham, 1994) and these have been confirmed for the common toad by more detailed habitat investigations (Latham, 1997). Over recent years broad categories of land use have been devised incorporating agricultural, physical and natural vegetation features (Bunce et al., 1981) which are potentially valuable for assessing overall amphibian habitat availability but are too recent to use in determining long-term habitat trends. Land use statistics for most of the country are restricted to agricultural classification.

Agricultural policies during and immediately after the Second World War resulted in dramatic changes in land use, involving the incorporation of uncultivated land into agriculture, and the conversion of pasture to arable use (e.g. Figure 7). There was a resultant deterioration in terrestrial amphibian habitat, as well as pond destruction. The area featured in Figure 7 is an extreme example, but the overall pattern in England and Wales is illustrated by Figure 8, showing a clear national trend towards increased arable land use. The impact of intensive agricultural land use on amphibians is dramatically illustrated in Figure 9, showing an area of Leicestershire in 1982 with 17 ponds, most of them apparently suitable as breeding sites, at least for the common frog and the smooth newt, but with only one pond occupied.

Additional indirect evidence on the suitability of habitat for amphibians in the UK is available from the statistics on land drainage. Land drainage can be expected to affect both breeding sites and the quality of terrestrial habitat. The extent of drainage in England and Wales increased steadily after the Second World War, from about 25,000 acres in 1950 to ten times that level in the early 1970's (Best and Coppock, 1972).

Changes in amphibian status

Changes in amphibian status since the Second World War are well documented (e.g. Beebee, 1973, Presst, Cooke & Corbett, 1974, Beebee, 1975, Cooke & Scorgie, 1983). These surveys coincide with the period of aquatic and terrestrial habitat deterioration, noted above. The clear overall trend is for declines in all species, especially those with relatively specialised requirements, like the natterjack toad and the crested newt.

Historical perspective

Most of the early pond surveys shown in Figure 1 are associated with the first series of Ordnance Survey maps, dated about 1880. This coincides with a period when pond numbers were probably at an all time high. As a result of the Acts of Enclosure field enclosures were created, in the main, between 1750 and 1820 and ponds introduced into many of them to provide water for stock. This also coincides with the period following the industrial revolution, when many ponds were created as an indirect result of the extraction of minerals such as clay and gravel, in northwest England, for example. Man is responsible for the occurrence of the majority of ponds in this country and before the 18th century they were much less common than today. It is difficult to conjecture as to pond numbers prior to the 18th century, in some areas they probably declined with progressive wetland drainage, in other areas they may have increased as a result of various management practices. These ideas are expressed in the lower part of Figure 10 where overall pond numbers are depicted as remaining relatively stable before 1700, rising to a peak about 1900, gradually declining until the Second World War and then declining rapidly after the war.

It is even more difficult to speculate on the suitability of the terrestrial habitat over time, but in this case it is suggested that the peak of suitability occurred sometime during the eighteenth century, discussed by Oldham (In press) and illustrated in Figure 10.

To summarise, it is suggested that the overall peak of amphibian habitat suitability occurred about one hundred years ago. At this time there were relatively few constraints, a high pond density being coupled with diverse terrestrial habitat in agricultural landscapes rich in hedges, ditches, wetland and woodland. All of our amphibian species were probably abundant. Even the enigmatic pool frog (*Rana lessonae*, Snell, 1994, Irving, 1995), a species adapted to marshland habitats, may have flourished at this time. Moving back in time from this "golden age", amphibian status was probably increasingly restricted by a shortage of suitable breeding sites, whilst moving forwards the effects of agricultural management had an increasingly damaging impact in both habitats, perhaps reaching a nadir about 1980.

Future prospects

The trends suggested for the current century in Figure 10 are discouraging and there is no doubt that amphibian populations in many parts of the country are under threat. In some parts of the country populations are probably restricted mainly by deficiencies in the terrestrial habitat, especially in areas with a predominance of arable agriculture (e.g. Figure 9), in others mainly by a shortage of ponds, as in some regions of Scotland, and in yet others by deficiencies in both habitats, as in intensively managed agricultural areas, East Anglia for example. Nevertheless, during the last decade a number of developments encourage us to hope that the outlook for amphibians and other pond dwellers is brighter than at any time since the Second World War. There is some evidence of reduced intensity of agricultural land use with the introduction of policies such as "set-aside", the reduction in fertiliser and pesticide use (Chalmers *et al.*, 1990) and the encouragement of diverse farming practices, including the introduction of ponds for fish and water fowl (MAFF, 1985, ADAS, 1986a, 1986b). Overall there is, perhaps, a more conservation-minded approach to farming and to the environment as a whole, with initiatives such as those associated with Local Agenda 21, with increased stringency in planning controls and measures for species protection (including two of the amphibian species) and with community-based conservation projects such as the *Pond Life Project* and the *Heritage Ponds Project*.

One of the latest surveys of the amphibians (Hilton-Brown & Oldham, 1991), covering the ten years of the 1980's, used an identical approach to that of Cooke & Scorgie (1983) ten years earlier. The two surveys canvassed the opinions of informed herpetologists on the changes in status of the five common amphibians during the previous decade, many of the same observers contributing to both. The British Isles was divided into 12 regions and, for each species, there were records from at least 8 of these in the 1970's, 10 in the 1980's. The crested newt showed declines in 75% of the regions in the 1970's (some severe declines), 70% in the 1980's (no severe declines). Most of the other species in both surveys showed either no change or an increase in status in the majority of regions; for the common toad 50% in the 1970's, 75% in the 1980's, for the palmate newts 90% & 80% respectively, for the smooth newt 73% and 91%, for the common frog 83% and 100%. It seems, therefore, for most of the species that there are modest signs of improvement in status. If this is a true reflection of trends it supports the above suggestions of habitat amelioration.

References

A.D.A.S. (1986a) *Management & maintenance of farm ponds.* M.A.F.F. leaflet **P3025**: Newcastle.

A.D.A.S. (1986b) *Farm ponds : design and construction.* M.A.F.F. leaflet **P3026**: Newcastle.

Arntzen J.W. & Wallis G.P. (1991) Restricted gene flow in a moving hybrid zone of the newts *Triturus cristatus* and *T. marmoratus* in Western France. *Evolution.* **45**: 805-826.

Banks B. & Laverick G. (1986). Garden ponds as amphibian breeding sites in a conurbation in north-east of England (Sunderland, Tyne & Wear). *Herpetological J.* **1**: 44-50.

Barr C.J., Howard, D.C. & Benefield C.B. (1994) *Countryside survey 1990. Inland water bodies.* Dept. of Environment: London.

Beebee T.J.C., (1973) Observations concerning the decline of the British amphibia. *Biological Conservation.* **5**: 20-24.

Beebee T.J.C., (1975) Changes in the status of the great crested newt *Triturus cristatus* in the British Isles. *Brit. J. Herpetology.* **5**: 481-490.

Beebee T.J.C., (1979) Habitats of the British amphibians (2) Suburban parks and gardens. *Biological Conservation.* **15**: 241-257.

Best R.H. & Coppock J.T., (1972) *The changing use of land in Britain.* Faber & Faber: London.

Bunce R.G.H., Barr C.J., Whittaker H.A. (1981) An integrated system of land classification. Institute of Terrestrial Ecology Annual Report for 1980: Grange-over-Sands.

Chalmers A., Kershaw C. & Leech P. (1990) Fertiliser use on farm crops in Great Britain: Results from the survey of fertiliser practice, 1969-88. *Outlook on agriculture* **19**: 269-278.

Cooke A.S. & Scorgie H.R.A., (1983) *The status of the commoner amphibians and reptiles in Britain.* Focus on Nature Conservation No 3. Nature Conservancy Council: Peterborough.

Hilton-Brown D. and Oldham R.S. (1991) *The status of the commoner amphibians and reptiles in Britain, 1990 and changes during the 1980s.* Contract Survey No.131. Nature Conservancy Council: Peterborough.

Irving B., (1995) Status of the pool frog *Rana lessonae* Camerano, as a native British species, based on zooarchaeological evidence from the English fens. Technical report of the Environmental Archaeology Unit, University of York, No.95/30.

Jones N.L. (1990) The effects of agriculture on ponds within two contrasting parishes of Leicestershire. Unpublished report, De Montfort University: Leicester.

Langton T. (1991) Distribution and status of reptiles and amphibians in the London area. *The London Naturalist.* **70**: 97-124.

Latham D.M. (1997) The terrestrial habitat selection and utilisation by the common toad (*Bufo bufo* L.) in agricultural landscapes. Unpublished Ph.D. thesis, De Montfort University: Leicester.

Latham D.M., Bowen J. & Jeffcote M. (1994) A revised study of amphibians in garden ponds in Leicestershire. *Trans. Leicestershire Literary and Philosophical Soc.* **88**: 20-24.

Martin J. (1993) The impact of government intervention on agricultural productivity in England and Wales, 1939-45. Unpublished Ph.D. thesis, Reading University: Reading.

Messenger G. (1971) *Flora of Rutland.* Leicester Museums & Art Gallery: Leicester.

Ministry of Agriculture Fisheries and Food (1985) *Survey of environmental topics on farms in England and Wales.* M.A.F.F. publications.

Oldham R.S. (1985) Toad dispersal in agricultural habitats. *Bull. Brit. Ecol. Soc.* **16**: 211-213.

Oldham R.S. (In Press) Amphibians and agriculture: double jeopardy. In: *Aquatic life cycle strategies.* Inst. of Biology.

Oldham R.S. & Swan M.J.S. (1991) Conservation of amphibian populations in Britain. In: Seitz A. & Loeschcke V. (Eds.) *Species conservation: A population-biological approach.* Birkhauser Verlag, Basel: 141-158.

Oldham R.S. & Swan, M.J.S. (1995) Pond loss, the present position. In: *Protecting Britain's Ponds.* Ed. Biggs J. & Aistrop, C., Pond Conservation Group: Oxford.

Presst I., Cooke A.S. & Corbett K.F. (1974) British amphibians and reptiles. In: Hawksworth D.L. (Ed.) *The changing flora and fauna of Britain.* Academic Press: London.

Reading C.J., Loman L. & Madsen T. (1991) Breeding pond fidelity in the common toad, *Bufo bufo. J. Zool. London.* **225**: 201-211.

Snell C., (1994) The pool frog - a neglected native? *Brit. Wildlife* **5**: 1-4.

Swan M.J.S. (1986) The conservation ecology of *Rana temporaria* and *Bufo bufo* in Leicestershire. Unpublished Ph.D. thesis, De Montfort University: Leicester.

Swan, M.J.S. & Oldham, R.S. (1993) *National amphibian survey.* English Nature Research Report No. **38**. English Nature: Peterborough.

Swan, M.J.S. & Oldham, R.S. (1994) Amphibians and landscape composition. In: Dover J. (Ed) *Fragmentation in agricultural landscapes. Proc. 3rd. Annual Conf. of International Assoc. Landscape Ecol.*: Preston.

Fig.1 Periods covered by surveys

a) Sources in literature

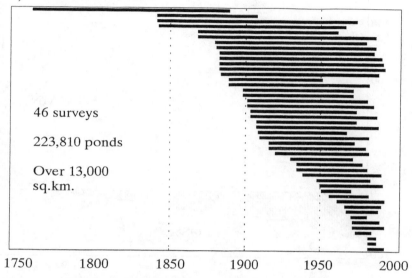

46 surveys

223,810 ponds

Over 13,000
sq.km.

1750   1800   1850   1900   1950   2000

b) National Amphibian Survey

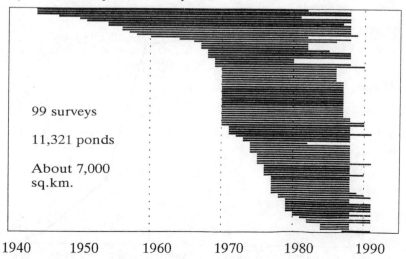

99 surveys

11,321 ponds

About 7,000
sq.km.

1940   1950   1960   1970   1980   1990

11

Fig. 2 Changes in pond numbers during the periods of survey

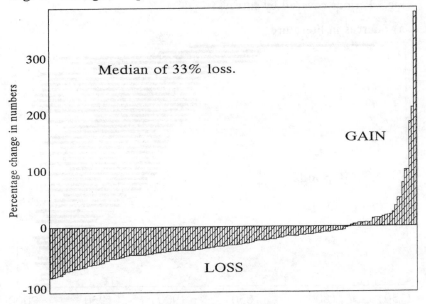

Fig.3 Decline of pond numbers in the parish of Horninghold, Leicestershire (After Jones, 1990)

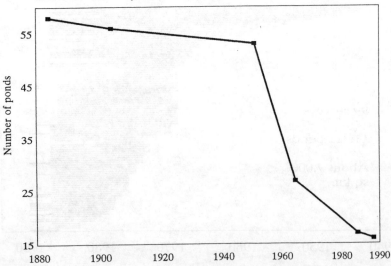

Fig.4 Annual changes in numbers of ponds during the periods of
137 surveys   a) Individual surveys (*: Barr et al.1990)

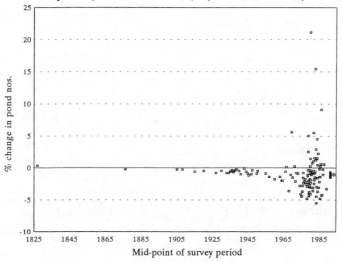

Mid-point of survey period

b) Medians within ten year groups

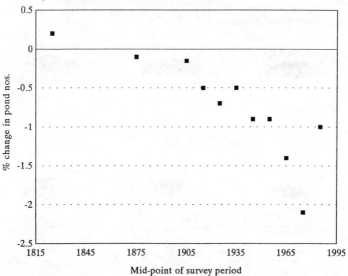

Mid-point of survey period

Fig.5 Examples of pond densities from early and recent surveys
(ponds per sq. km)

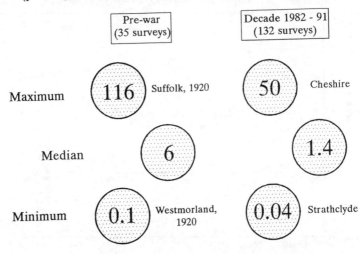

Pre-war
(35 surveys)

Decade 1982 - 91
(132 surveys)

Maximum
116 — Suffolk, 1920
50 — Cheshire

Median
6
1.4

Minimum
0.1 — Westmorland, 1920
0.04 — Strathclyde

Fig.6 Relative incidence of pond use by common amphibians,
with corresponding effective pond densities and mean
inter-pond distances for each species

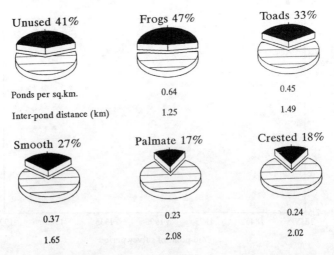

Unused 41%   Frogs 47%   Toads 33%

Ponds per sq.km.   0.64   0.45
Inter-pond distance (km) 1.25   1.49

Smooth 27%   Palmate 17%   Crested 18%

0.37   0.23   0.24
1.65   2.08   2.02

Fig.7 Land use changes in Rutland, 1866 to 1966
(After Messenger, 1971)

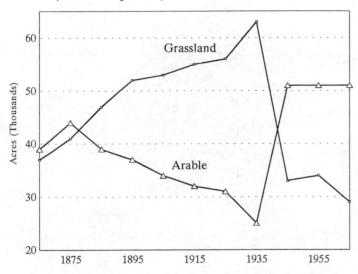

Fig.8 The distribution of arable land in England & Wales in 1939 & 1944, by county (after Martin, 1993)

15

Fig.9   Agricultural land in part of Leicestershire with
only one pond occupied by amphibians (from Swan, 1986)

Fig.10   Speculated changes in amphibian habitat quality
(from Oldham, In press)

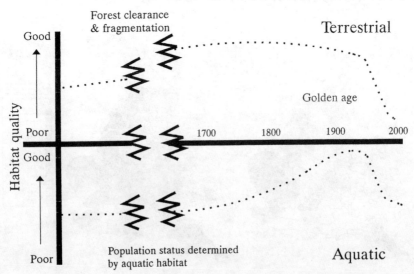

16

Ponds and other small water-bodies in North-West England: an audit.

J. Boothby

Pond *Life* Project, Liverpool John Moores University, Trueman Building,
15-21 Webster St, Liverpool, L3 2ET

Abstract

An audit of small water-bodies in North-west England reveals that there are 13000 containing open water and over 14000 in a state of advanced vegetational succession. Since the 1870s, the total number of ponds has fallen by c. 61%. Their present distribution across the component administrative Districts of the region is shown, and explanation for the pattern advanced; attention is also given to the cohesiveness of the pond landscape. The broad character of biodiversity revealed by sample surveys is described and a map of 'core pondscape' derived.

Introduction

As part of the Pond *Life* Project (Boothby *et al.*, 1995) an audit of all water bodies of area 2 ha or less has been undertaken for North-West England. The sources for the audit have been various editions of the 1:10,560 / 1:10,000 Ordnance Survey maps, augmented by: (i) aerial photography carried out on behalf of various Local Authorities; (ii) detailed biological sample surveys [see Guest, this volume]; (iii) local records; and (iv) volunteer ground survey. Though survey in the close environs of Greater Manchester and Liverpool is incomplete, the audit provides systematic evidence from Britain's pond stronghold, covering 5779 km^2, including two complete Counties (Cheshire and Lancashire) comprising 24 Districts. The areas not so far fully audited are known to include a large number of man-made features such as old mill lodges, small reservoirs, and industrial pools.

Methods and limitations.

Locations of all pond sites were digitised from Ordnance Survey [OS] source maps into a GIS in pcArcInfo. For each site, records of pond status were kept in a related database: aerial photographs were inspected for all sites allowing the classification of each pond as "wet" , "overgrown", or "lost"; where possible, the cause of loss was ascertained. From other activities of the Project, pond habitat and related site information, including detailed species records, were attached to the database. As information in the GIS is derived from a variety of sources of different dates, all information reported here is approximate, but, it is felt, very reliable (Boothby & Hull, 1997). Though there are some sources of bias in this type of survey (eg: accuracy of the OS source maps; completeness of digitising; characteristics of the aerial photography), it seems likely that omissions from the survey will tend to be: (i) smaller ponds; (ii) seasonal ponds; (iii) ponds in urban areas; (iv) moorland pools. All in all, the audit may be a slight underestimate by 1% or less. Work is in hand to refine this figure.

Table 1: **Status of pond sites determined from aerial photography**

County/ District	Extant sites n	Pond present n	%	Over- shaded or -vegetated n	%
Lancashire County[+]	8930	4606	51.6	4324	48.4
Blackburn	193	125	64.8	68	35.2
Blackpool	69	65	94.2	4	5.8
Burnley	57	42	73.7	15	16.3
Chorley	1284	538	41.9	746	58.1
Fylde	1446	941	65.1	505	34.9
Hyndburn	94	85	73.7	9	9.6
Lancaster	525	269	51.2	256	48.8
Pendle	56	50	89.3	6	10.7
Preston	1219	528	43.3	691	56.7
Ribble Valley	772	358	46.4	414	53.6
Rossendale	168	141	83.9	27	16.1
South Ribble	595	283	47.6	312	52.4
West Lancashire	1055	433	41.0	622	59.0
Wyre	1397	748	53.5	649	46.5
Wigan MBC[+]	835	498	60.0	337	40.0

The current status of the ponds

The above methods show there to be 12925 wet ponds in the audited parts of the region, an overall density of 2.24 km^{-2}. In addition, there are a further 14383 ponds in a state of advanced vegetational succession. From more detailed studies carried out in Cheshire (Boothby & Hull, 1997), it is estimated that this same audit area had, in the 1870s (around the time of the first detailed mapping by the Ordnance Survey) some 80000 ponds, most of which were unencumbered by overshading trees and other tall vegetation. Using this base-line, then, the loss of pond-sites has been 61%; perhaps more critically, of those ponds that remain, only about 47 % retain open water. Though all successional stages of ponds provide habitat, the nature of that habitat has clearly changed significantly over the past 125 years: the implications of some of these changes will be examined elsewhere in this volume. Several conclusions follow: without intervention, the size of the resource will decline, pond landscape fragmentation will increase, habitats will change in relative importance, and there will be consequences for pond-reliant species and for the distinctive regional landscapes.

Table 1   (continued)

County/ District	Extant sites n	Pond present n	%	Over- shaded or -vegetated n	%
Cheshire County *	16728	7558	46.2	9170	54.8
Chester City	3974	1978	49.8	1996	50.2
Congleton	1765	689	64.0	1076	36.0
Crewe & N'wich	3280	1731	52.8	1549	47.2
EllesmerePt& Nn	445	155	34.8	290	65.2
Halton	295	140	47.5	155	52.5
Macclesfield	3671	1342	36.6	2329	63.4
Vale Royal	2478	1126	45.4	1352	54.6
Warrington	858	396	46.2	462	53.8
Wirral MBC*	816	263	32.2	553	67.8
Audit Area Total@	27309	12925	47.3	14384	52.7

Notes: * Data derived from aerial survey 1992/3; + Data derived from aerial survey 1988.
@ Excludes unaudited Districts of Merseyside and of Greater Manchester.

Visualising the resource

The pond resource of North-West England is largely, but not entirely, confined to the lowlands, though moorland pools, old mining reservoirs, and other water-bodies also exist on the higher ground. These lowland marl, clay and other pits had been excavated in the period up to 1830. Relationships can readily be traced with the Drift geology and soils of the region; significant "gaps" in the distribution may also be found to be related to urban and industrial concentrations. Figure 1 shows the resource, using the Local Authority District boundaries. Each circle is scaled to represent the total number of pond-sites and then divided in proportion to the "wet" and "overgrown" components. As seen, and as supported by Table 1, most Districts have more than two-fifths of their ponds over-vegetated. Sample survey evidence (Pond *Life* Project, 1997) details those plant species implicated in vegetational succession (Table 2).

Pond persistence and pond character.

Information on the persistence of ponds in the landscape permits the examination of causes of loss. Detailed statistical information on this is currently available for the south of the region (Cheshire & Wirral) only. Here, high loss rates have been shown to be associated with rapid urbanisation of the countryside by housing, industry, and commercial development (Boothby

Table 2:   Potential dominants of swamp and wooded pond vegetation
            (Occurring in >5% of ponds)

		Sampled Ponds (n=492)	
Species	Common name	Occurrences	%
Sparganium erectum	Branched Bur-reed	234	47.6
Glyceria fluitans	Floating Sweet-grass	216	43.9
Salix cinerea	Common Sallow	210	42.7
Phalaris arundinacea	Reed Canary-grass	169	34.3
Typha latifolia	Greater Reedmace	142	28.9
Equisetum fluvilatile	Water Horsetail	107	21.8
Eleocharis palustris	Common Spike-rush	97	19.7
Carex pseudocyperus	Cyperus Sedge	94	19.1
Alnus glutinosa	Alder	93	18.9
Salix fragilis	Crack Willow	73	14.8
Carex otrubae	False Fox-sedge	25	5.1

and Hull, 1997). The total number of ponds lost is, reasonably enough, highest on that agricultural land with the highest concentrations of such features. Certain parts of the region have managed to retain a large proportion of open, wet water-bodies, These exceptional districts include those with significant amount of high moorland (Hyndburn, Pendle, Rossendale, and Burnley) and the equally exposed district of Blackpool. However, these five districts have between them only 450 ponds of all descriptions! In the lowland Districts, very many ponds are overvegetated - West Lancashire (59%), Preston (57%), Ellesmere Port (65%), Macclesfield (63%), and Wirral (68%) represent this extreme. It is suspected that rapid overgrowth is associated with smaller average pond size, but this has not yet been specifically tested.

Certainly, the ponds demonstrate considerable variety in their physiographic, hydrological, hydrochemical and other characteristics. The size of the surveyed ponds varies between $12m^2$ and $11,700 \text{ m}^2$, with an average size of 918 m^2 (Table 3). Measurement of depth is quite difficult, as many ponds have thick layers of silt: two-thirds of ponds have a silt depth of over 0.5 m. Though few ponds are connected to true natural streams, many are supplied (or drained) by ditches or other field drains, and are thus in danger of receiving considerable agricultural run-off. Water pH (measured only in the latter stages of the survey) averages at 7.24, with an inter-quartile range of $6.88 < pH < 8.04$.

Biological Status

The biological status of the region's ponds is currently the subject of detailed analysis, in which the associations between hydrology, physiography, hydrochemistry, and species presence will form a substantial element. But it is possible here to sketch some of the profile of variation, using a large sample survey (Pond *Life* Project, 1997); more detail is given in Guest (*this volume*) and in Boothby (*this volume*: Species records in the Biodiversity surveys of the Pond *Life* Project).

Figure 1: Pond status by District.

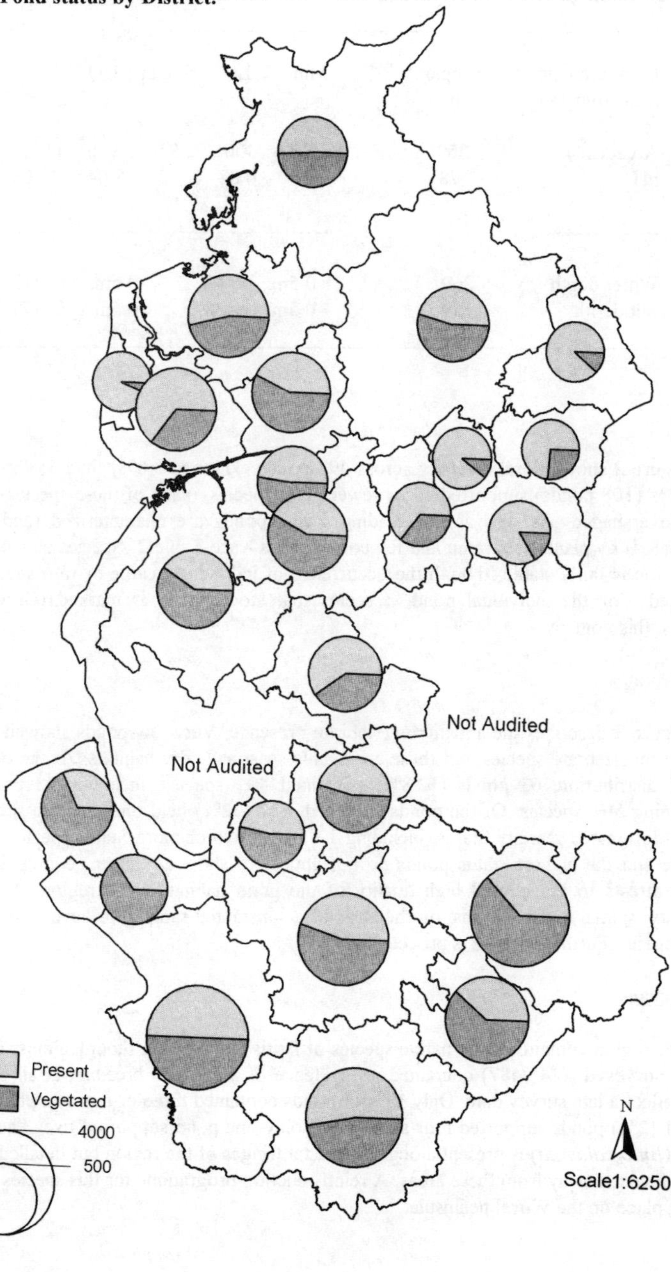

Not Audited

Not Audited

Present
Vegetated

4000
500

N

Scale1:625000

21

Table 3: Some physical and hydrochemical characteristics of sampled ponds

Characteristic/ measurement	sample n	Min.	LQ	Mean	UQ	Max.
Area (m²)	269	12.0	300	918	936	11700
pH	78	3.55	6.88	7.24	8.04	10.05
----------------			--			
Water depth	269	<0.5m: n=42		>0.5m: n=212		
Silt depth	269	<0.5m: n=88		>0.5m: n=171		

Plants

Figure 2 shows floral diversity across 492 ponds: 31 ponds (6%) had 35+ plant species, but 22% (108 ponds) supported 13 or fewer plant species; many of these species-poor ponds were overshaded. As well as overshading, many ponds are characterized (and sometimes dominated) by plants of swamp and fen communities - see Table 2. Species abundance across the region is fairly stable, though the occurrence of individual scarce or rare species is more localised. For the individual pond, it seems that stochasticity is marked (Grayson, 1994; Jeffries, this volume).

Invertebrates

Figure 3 describes the aquatic invertebrate presence. Very few ponds showed a complete lack of invertebrate species, but these are mainly seasonally dry habitats. At the opposite end of the distribution, 63 ponds (12.8%) contained 40+ species, including 13 ponds (2.6%) containing 50+ species. Of the ponds surveyed, 157 (32%) held one or more species with a JNCC-designated scarcity Status, including 12% with two or more Status species. The most diverse and the highest status ponds do not appear to show any clear geographical pattern, which attests to the overall high quality of the pond habitat in the region. As in floristic diversity, spatial pattern seems, on the basis of a substantial sample, to have a strong random component. Further analysis is proceeding.

Amphibians

The region contains all six native species of British amphibian, though almost one-third of ponds surveyed (146/487) contained no evidence of amphibian breeding at all; in part, this may reflect a late survey date. Only 13% of ponds contained three or more amphibian species, just 11 (2%) ponds supported four species and only one pond supported five. The Natterjack Toad (*Bufo calamita*) is present along the coastal fringes of the region but detailed survey has so far focused away from these areas. A reintroduction programme for this species is currently taking place on the Wirral peninsula.

Figure 2   Flora diversity (n=492 ponds)

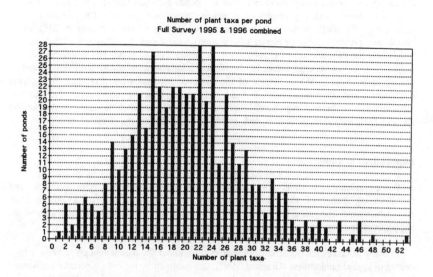

Number of plant taxa per pond
Full Survey 1995 & 1996 combined

Figure 3   Number of invertebrate species per pond (n= 492 ponds)

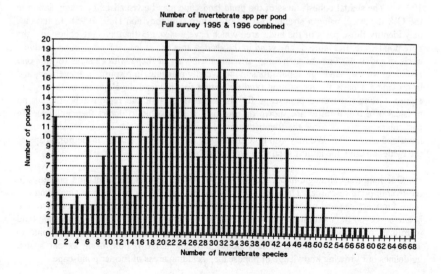

Number of invertebrate spp per pond
Full survey 1995 & 1996 combined

The region is one of the European strongholds of the Great Crested Newt *(Triturus cristatus)*, the species being found in 126 of 487 ponds surveyed (26%). The species is found in 37% of ponds with any amphibian presence ["amphibian ponds"]. The species is more common in the south of the region (Cheshire & Wirral) where it occurs in 51% of all "amphibian ponds". Smooth Newts (*T. vulgaris*) were found in 102 ponds (21%), and 13 ponds held the Palmate Newt (*T. helveticus*). A further 21% of ponds had undifferentiated *T. vulgaris* / *T. helveticus* eggs and/or larvae, without adults being recorded; the Palmate Newt is known to be more common outside of the surveyed lowland areas. Common Frog *(Rana temporaria)* and Common Toad *(B. bufo)* breed throughout the region, being present in c. 40% and 23% of ponds respectively (but see Guest, this volume). Whereas *R. temporaria* shows a fairly even distribution, *B. bufo* seems more common in the North of the region.

Implications of audit

Work is in hand to consider more carefully the relationship between species occurrence and the changing status of the North-west pond resource, in order to develop a truly comprehensive conservation framework. From the work reported here, I wish to focus on the implications deriving from geographical distribution of species and habitats.

In many instances the occurrence of species throughout the region appears to show a high degree of spatial randomness (Grayson, 1994); this seems to be the case especially for winged invertebrates and for plants, whose colonisation capabilities are only little restricted by distance between ponds. For amphibians, however, the connectivity of the pond resource may be important to population persistence. Fragmentation, isolation, inhospitable terrestrial habitat - all play a role in reducing the colonisation and recolonisation probabilities (Ebenhart, 1991). The spatial cohesiveness of the pond landscape may be visualised by manipulation in the GIS database, using a straightforward procedure (Boothby and Hull, 1995). In this, we may identify those parts of the audit area which have a stronger than average cohesion - the core pondscape. In Figure 4, any pond in the shaded area has at least 15 other ponds within a circle of radius 1000m. As such a representation will vary in shape with changes to the pond resource, we may envisage applications in biodiversity planning, in resource management, and in providing a basis for monitoring (and mitigating for) physical development in the region. Figure 4 shows the core pondscape for the northern part of the region only; though no physical or urban features are shown on this map, it is possible to detect their influence. In particular, we may observe the fragmentation of the pondscape to the east as ground rises to moorland over 300m. We may also note the largely unfragmented nature of the pondscape of the Fylde, possibly the largest such structure in the North West.

One important strategic implication is that we should combat fragmentation pressures in the overall pond resource. This could be achieved by a variety of mechanisms, including site renovation, active pond management, and the creation of new ponds and associated terrestrial habitats.. Given the mounting evidence against the hitherto assumed value of wholesale (and uncritical) renovation of ponds (Biggs *et al.*, 1994), there should be significant value in attempting to create a tranche of new ponds throughout the region, using as our spatial guidelines our growing knowledge of pondscape, including areas of former pondscape.

The region is one of the European strongholds of the Great Crested Newt *(Triturus cristatus)*, the species being found in 126 of 487 ponds surveyed (26%). The species is found in 37% of ponds with any amphibian presence ["amphibian ponds"]. The species is more common in the south of the region (Cheshire & Wirral) where it occurs in 51% of all "amphibian ponds". Smooth Newts *(T. vulgaris)* were found in 102 ponds (21%), and 13 ponds held the Palmate Newt *(T. helveticus)*. A further 21% of ponds had undifferentiated *T. vulgaris / T. helveticus* eggs and/or larvae, without adults being recorded. The Palmate Newts is known to be more common outside of the surveyed lowland areas. Common Frog *(Rana temporaria)* and Common Toad *(B. bufo)* breed throughout the region, being present in c. 40% and 23% of ponds respectively (but see Guest, this volume). Whereas *R. temporaria* shows a fairly even distribution, *B. bufo* seems more common in the North of the region.

Implications of audit

Work is in hand to consider more carefully the relationship between species occurrence and the changing status of the North-west pond resource, in order to develop a truly comprehensive conservation framework. From the work reported here, I wish to focus on the implications deriving from geographical distribution of species and habitats.

In many instances the occurrence of species throughout the region appears to show a high degree of spatial randomness (Grayson, 1994); this seems to be the case especially for winged invertebrates and for plants, whose colonisation capabilities are only little restricted by distance between ponds. For amphibians, however, the connectivity of the pond resource may be important to population persistence. Fragmentation, isolation, inhospitable terrestrial habitat - all play a role in reducing the colonisation and recolonisation probabilities (Ebenhart, 1991). The spatial cohesiveness of the pond landscape may be visualised by manipulation in the GIS database, using a straightforward procedure (Boothby and Hull, 1995). In this, we may identify those parts of the audit area which have a stronger than average cohesion - the core pondscape. In Figure 4, any pond in the shaded area has at least 15 other ponds within a circle of radius 1000m. As such a representation will vary in shape with changes to the pond resource, we may envisage applications in biodiversity planning, in resource management, and in providing a basis for monitoring (and mitigating for) physical development in the region. Figure 4 shows the core pondscape for the northern part of the region only; though no physical or urban features are shown on this map, it is possible to detect their influence. In particular, we may observe the fragmentation of the pondscape to the east as ground rises to moorland over 300m. We may also note the largely unfragmented nature of the pondscape of the Fylde, possibly the largest such structure in the North West.

One important strategic implication is that we should combat fragmentation pressures in the overall pond resource. This could be achieved by a variety of mechanisms, including site renovation, active pond management, and the creation of new ponds and associated terrestrial habitats.. Given the mounting evidence against the hitherto assumed value of wholesale (and uncritical) renovation of ponds (Biggs *et al.*, 1994), there should be significant value in attempting to create a tranche of new ponds throughout the region, using as our spatial guidelines our growing knowledge of pondscape, including areas of former pondscape.

Figure 4: The pondscape of Lancashire.

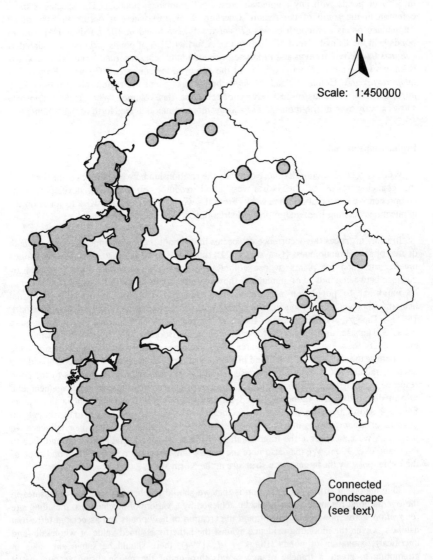

N

Scale: 1:450000

Connected
Pondscape
(see text)

Acknowledgments

The Pond *Life* Project is a conservation demonstration project supported by the *Life* Programme of the EU, led by Liverpool John Moores University, in a consortium of UK and European partners. Biological survey was carried out by Jonathan Guest Ecological Survey, and reported in Pond *Life* Project (1997) from which Figures 2 and 3 are reproduced. Maps for this paper have been produced by Jon Bloor.

Email: j.boothby@livjm.ac.uk

References.

Biggs, J.; Corfield, A.; Walker, D.; Whitfield, M. and Williams, P. (1994) New approaches to the management of ponds. *British Wildlife*, **5**: 273-287.

Boothby, J. & Hull, A.P. (1995) Mapping Cheshire's ponds. *Bulletin, Society of University Cartographers*, **29.1**: 13-17.

Boothby, J., Hull, A.P. & Jeffreys, D.A. (1995) Sustaining a threatened landscape: farmland ponds in Cheshire. *Journal of Environmental Planning and Management*, **38**: 561-568.

Boothby, J. & Hull, A.P. (1997) A census of ponds in Cheshire, North-west England. *Aquatic Conservation: Marine and Freshwater Ecosystems*, **7**: 75-79.

Ebenhart, T. (1991) Colonisation in metapopulations: a review of theory and observations. *Biological Journal of the Linnean Society*, **42**: 105-121.

Grayson, R. (1994) The distribution and conservation of the ponds of North-west England. *Lancashire Wildlife Journal*, **263**: 23-51.

Pond *Life* Project (1997) *Critical Pond Biodiversity Survey 1996*, Pond *Life* Project, Liverpool John Moores University (Unpublished survey report).

School Ponds : their current status and likely contribution to education, conservation
and local environmental enhancement

M.R. Braund

Bretton Hall College of The University of Leeds, West Bretton, Wakefield, WF4 4LG, UK

Abstract

School ponds have a considerable history and in recent years have become a
common feature of school grounds, particularly in the primary sector.
Relatively little is known about their status and effectiveness educationally and
in terms of conservation value.

This paper reports the findings of a survey involving 46 schools in ten different
Local Education Authorities (LEAs). The findings show that factors
constraining schools from developing ponds, the ways in which they have come
about and are managed and used, vary markedly between primary and secondary
schools.

The design, maintenance and amenity value of school ponds result in a number
of compromises. These may be problematic in terms of conservation value but
have to be resolved in an educational setting.

Introduction

The emphasis on school ground use in the first half of this century was purely for
recreation and games (Board of Education, 1933). Since the early 1950s, however, there has
been a steady shift away from this position to encompass more aesthetic and environmental
aspects. School building bulletins produced by the Department for Education and Science
(DES) for example recommended that children should ... "have small private gardens,
perhaps a pond, perhaps some accommodation for animals" (DES, 1955). Children
themselves have also been found to value bodies of water in the design of their school's
environment (Manchester Polytechnic, 1977).

Over the last twenty years the growth in school ponds has been accelerated by a number
of influences; the increasing ecological content of examination syllabuses, the introduction
of a National Curriculum in England and Wales, promotion of school grounds development
by LEAs and bodies awarding grants for the development of school grounds (e.g. English
Nature, Groundwork Trust etc.). This growth has coincided with a marked decline in the
number of ponds found in the natural environment - a rate estimated at 2% per annum
(Oldham and Swan, 1994). The recent increase in school ponds is paralleled by an even
greater one for garden ponds and these are seen by some as making an important

contribution to the conservation of freshwater habitats in urban areas, particularly for amphibian populations (Latham, 1995). In this way school ponds form part of a crucial network of freshwater sites that enhance local environments. This is particularly true where schools have been built on previous farmland and in central urban areas of high density building where ponds are rare.

Whilst there is much published advice on the building of school ponds (see for example, Brooks and Agate, 1997; Sansom, 1993; Kersey, 1997) there has been little published research into the effectiveness of school ponds in terms of conservation, educational use and maintenance. Evaluations have been carried out at a local level (e.g. Kirklees Metropolitan Council, 1995) but these have usually formed the basis of reports to the funding body to highlight 'success rates' or 'value for money'. The purpose of the research described in this paper is to fill a gap and act as the first stage in a national project raising the profile of school ponds as an educational resource and advising schools, governing bodies and other interested parties as to their best use.

The survey and its main findings

The scope and design of the survey

A questionnaire was designed to elicit information from a wide variety of schools in both the primary and secondary sectors. Bretton Hall College has links with schools, via its school partnership schemes, in ten LEAs across the Yorkshire region. Sixty-four primary schools were chosen on the basis of those hosting second year undergraduate students on teaching practice. Students left the questionnaires with the school for return to the College. A similar number of secondary schools in the partnership scheme were sent the questionnaire by post.

The questionnaire was divided into four sections. Questions were based mainly on a limited range of options and followed best advice on design in terms of validity, readability and avoidance of ambiguity (Oppenheim, 1992). The first section asked for basic background information on school location and size and the age of any pond. Questions in the following section probed the development and maintenance of the pond and the frequency of its use by different groups of children. The third section asked for a limited amount of physical and biotic data. The final section was designed for those schools who did not have ponds with the intention of measuring the relative importance of factors preventing construction.

The status of school ponds

Response rates and number of ponds

Just over one third of the schools contacted replied and although this is less than was hoped for it is acceptable in the context of the exploratory phase of the project. Response rates were similar in both primary and secondary sectors.

A high proportion of all schools (65%) reported having ponds; 56% of primary schools and 74% of secondary schools. This is almost certainly not representative of schools in general and probably biased by the fact that schools with successful ponds or those having problems with them wanted to inform the project. This was particularly true for secondary schools.

Types, ages and sizes of ponds

Most school ponds were purpose built and often planned as part of a wildlife area containing a variety of habitats (e.g. meadow, copse, habitat/log piles). A few ponds were built as part of the original construction or extension to a school. These are often ornamental features. One secondary school reported sharing a large natural pond as part of a co-managed wetland reserve. As predicted from recent trends, school ponds are relatively recent, over 80% being less than 15 years old. Some are very recent, less than two years old and these are likely to be replacements for vandalised or leaking ponds, built in addition to existing features or are the result of recently funded projects.

Pond sizes are on the small side, 70% being less than 20m^2. The range of sizes however is very large from small, oval, garden-sized ponds of 2m^2 or less to larger constructions of over 150m^2. The largest ponds tend to be in secondary schools where space is not at such a premium. Most ponds are rarely over 1 metre in depth (mean maximum depth is 86cm). The shallowest ponds are around 30cm deep.

Factors constraining the development of school ponds

Schools without ponds were encouraged to reply to the questionnaire so that the potential for further use of the resource could be gauged and restricting factors examined.

Virtually all schools who replied but do not currently have ponds said that they wanted one. The factors that had highest priority in terms of constraints in the minds of respondents (scored 1 or 2 on a 1-5 scale) are displayed as table 1 below:

Table 1 Factors constraining schools from building ponds

	Percentage of schools giving each factor high priority		
	All schools n = 17	Primary schools n = 10	Secondary schools n = 7
Cost	71	90	43
Maintenance	41	40	43
Vandalism	59	40	86
Lack of Expertise	18	20	14
Space	6	10	0

It appears that cost is a major concern for schools especially for those in the primary sector. Maintenance is a problem for all schools and vandalism features strongly particularly in secondary schools.

The development, use and management of school ponds

Development and construction

Schools with ponds were asked to indicate sources of support and funding and also indicate if development was part of an overall plan. The results of this section of the survey are reported as table 2 shown below:

Table 2 Assistance and planning for the construction of school ponds

	All schools (%) n = 30	Primary schools (%) n = 13	Secondary schools (%) n = 17
Part of wildlife plan	46	38	53
Community group	16	23	12
LEA	10	15	6
Special grant	37	38	35
Parents	27	46	12
Children	63	62	65

Schools made good use of children particularly at the planning stage but parental involvement was much higher in the primary schools. It is perhaps surprising that few schools mentioned LEA involvement since at the very least planning departments must be consulted to check location of underground services and safety. Respondents may have been cued here to think that 'involvement' applied more to the active phases of construction, planting and aftercare than to planning and design.

Educational use

Schools were asked to say how intensively they used their ponds with different age groups during the year. Primary schools seemed to use their ponds more equitably across year groups. Half the schools said that all classes in a year group used the pond at some stage in the year compared with only 18% in secondary schools. Year round study featured in a quarter of primary schools but in only 6% of secondary school use. It seems that one or two teachers are more likely to use the resource in secondary schools and that this may be related to the demands of a particular examination syllabus.

Maintenance

Most ponds are managed to clear plants and maintain a mid-successional status by action at least once a year. About one third of schools reported managing their ponds on a more regular basis most often under the supervision of an enthusiastic teacher or parent or by the caretaker. Surprisingly few schools seemed to use children to assist in maintenance with the notable exception of four schools who reported the formation of wildlife/conservation 'action groups' to carry out this and other work in the school grounds.

<u>Pond populations</u>

Although schools were asked a number of questions as to the species present in their ponds, information is rather scant. This is primarily due to the lack of survey information retained from class use and/or problems with the knowledge base of teachers in this area particularly in the primary schools. Some interesting information regarding amphibian populations, however, has emerged.

Amphibians in school ponds

Nearly three quarters of schools with ponds reported having resident amphibian populations. The common frog (*Rana temporaria*) was reported in 70% of ponds and 'newts' (*Triturus sp.*) in 33%. One school reported the presence of the palmate newt (*Triturus helveticus*) although individuals may have been confused here with females of the smooth newt (*Triturus vulgaris*) as identification is notoriously difficult for non-experts (Latham, 1995). A school with shared use of a large adjacent pond as part of a wetland conservation scheme reported the presence of the great crested newt (*Triturus cristatus*).

Discussion of the findings and implications for more effective use of school ponds

The design of a school pond must consider a number of factors. These include; optimising wildlife potential and species diversity, amenity for data collection/pond dipping, safety and security and overall land use within the context of the school's locality, the nature and extent of its grounds and intended or past development. The consequent compromises mean that thorough planning and a good understanding of the features of effective design are prerequisites for success. There is evidence to show that developments fail where there is poor design and/or a lack of appreciation of the pond as a transient habitat undergoing continual succession (Kirklees Metropolitan Council, *op. cit.* p34-5).

<u>The siting of ponds</u>

Ponds are more likely to attract a greater diversity of invertebrate fauna and support amphibian populations where they are within semi-natural environments and close to woodland, copse or other vegetation (Latham, *op. cit.* p28, Pond Action, 1994). The siting of ponds within wildlife areas helps in this respect but these are still likely to be isolated from more substantial areas of vegetation. Some ponds have to be sited away from field margins and boundaries because of security and safety. Having a pond next to the school may make it more secure but less interesting in terms of faunal diversity. There is also the problem that if the pond is surrounded by a wildlife area in this situation it makes the aspect of the school look untidy. This has previously been reported as a worry by some schools (Adams, 1990).

Size, depth and open water

Although ponds tend to be small, this may not be a problem in terms of richness for study. There is evidence to show that small ponds are just as diverse as large ones (Biggs *et. al*, 1994). Maintaining the necessary degree of open water and access for pond dipping poses some interesting problems for designers.

The usual activity for children to carry out in school pond studies is to use relatively small nets and to reach out into accessible water to sweep for animals. Where ponds follow conventional design with sloping sides from shallower margins this can cause problems particularly in summer months when water has evaporated and the water edge is too far from the dipping position. One suggestion (Kersey, *op. cit.* p2) is to plan for slightly deeper water (to a maximum depth of 40 cm) planted with submerged plants at the edge of a dipping platform with a retaining board or rail so that children can reach safely to obtain sufficiently rich samples. The main marginal vegetation is then planted to a sloping edge adjacent or opposite the amenity.

Most recommendations on safety suggest maximum pond depths of 75-100 cm (Bunyan, 1988; Brooks and Agate *op. cit.* p48) and this is consistent with the findings quoted in this paper. There is value in having some deeper water as it allows for a refuge of unfrozen water in the severest winters and it is less likely that the pond will dry out completely in summer months although this may not be disastrous for many species (Pond Action, 1994).

Problems of security and vandalism

Damage to ponds through vandalism was a concern of many schools in the survey particularly secondary schools in central or peripheral urban situations. The most common damage is to pond liners soon after construction. Some advisers recommend a 'belt and braces' approach using a liner protected by a concrete armater (Brooks and Agate, *op. cit.* p 56-9). Such an approach is very costly and as the findings show this is the most sensitive aspect for schools. A cheaper solution is to lay a tough polyethylene matting over the liner and to ensure that this is secured and the pond filled in one session. The matting has the advantage that it cannot be cut with a sharp knife and that algal growth and plant rooting is swift therefore making it look natural within a short space of time.

One common source of attack is from rocks and other objects thrown into the pond which then puncture the lining. Simply removing rocks and debris from the site can do much to minimise this. Many schools have had problems with stone or concrete slabs laid to edge the pond or provide dipping platforms being thrown in soon after construction. These materials are therefore best avoided.

Maintenance - the management of vegetation

Survey findings show that maintenance continues to be a major problem for schools. Research carried out on behalf of Kirklees Local Education Authority (Kirklees Metropolitan Council, *op cit.* p32-3) shows that whilst half of all schools engaging in grounds development included ponds they were seen as more problematic than any other habitat/area of development. Schools are usually happy with ponds for about two years or so and indeed colonisation during this time is known to be relatively fast with most species likely to colonise present in this time and maximum diversity achieved five years from construction (Williams *et al.*, 1997).

The main problem for schools is the need to maintain the pond's amenity value for educational study and this inevitably requires management on a more regular basis than staff realise. The relatively small size of school ponds exacerbates the situation particularly where vigorous plants such as common reedmace (*Typha latifolia*) and Unbranched Bur-reed (*Sparganium simplex*) are present. Some schools buying plants from non-wildlife specialists or 'on the cheap' may have inadvertently introduced highly invasive alien species such as New Zealand Pygmyweed (*Crassula helmsii*). Good advice on suitable plants and reliable sources for these are given in a number of publications (see for example; Drake, Brooks and Agate, Kersey, *op. cit*).

Most schools in the survey reported that they managed their ponds only yearly or in response to 'crises'. A more regular and gentle regime may be more beneficial to the pond ecosystem as more drastic intervention is likely to lead to greater time for recovery or excessive removal of sites for invertebrates (Drake *et. al. op. cit.* p10-11).

Educational use

Some educators see satisfactory ecological understanding requiring study of ecosystems at all seasons (Tansley, 1987). The survey indicates that such studies at school ponds are rare particularly in the secondary schools yet arguably this is where the sophistication of knowledge and understanding required is greatest. The concentration of pond studies in summer months means intensive dipping by many classes over a short period of time and this may have consequences for the recovery of invertebrate populations particularly in small ponds. Kersey (*op. cit.*), for example, recommends that an area equivalent to at least one third of the pond is left undipped to allow for recovery and recolonisation in undisturbed areas.

Environmental education represents a much broader curriculum area than the study of ecology alone. The National Curriculum Council for example has recognised three basic aspects:

Education ABOUT the environment
Education THROUGH the environment
Education FOR the environment

(NCC, 1990 p7)

The last of these can best be achieved through the involvement of pupils in enhancement and maintenance of their own environment. It is perhaps surprising therefore that few schools involve children very directly or actively in the continued development and maintenance of their outside resources.

Conclusion

The research here shows that school ponds continue to be a popular resource for educational study and a first choice for many in the context of school grounds development. Schools that do not have ponds would like them but cost, vandalism and maintenance are real constraints. The difficult compromises necessary when designing and constructing school ponds result in choices that may not always benefit users or the pond ecosystem itself. More work remains to be done on the ways in which the intensity of pond dipping, siting, size and depth characteristics affect environmental quality of ponds.

School ponds may not make a major contribution in terms of locally or nationally rare species although detailed ecological assays are required to see if this is true. They are probably significant in terms of amphibian populations and contribute to the overall mosaic of ponds including the increasing number flourishing in local gardens. They therefore make a valuable contribution to the richness of freshwater sites particularly in depleted urban areas.

Ponds remain an increasingly useful resource for the education of children although schools could do more to manage and use the resource more effectively and involve children and the community in their conservation.

References

Adams, E. (1990) *Learning through landscapes. A report on the use, design, management and development of school grounds.* Learning Through Landscapes Trust, Winchester 79-157

Biggs, J.; Corfield, A.; Walker, D.; Whitfield, M. & Williams, P. (1994) New approaches to the management of ponds. *British Wildlife* 5: 273-287

Board of Education (1993) *Syllabus for physical training in schools.* Board of Education, London.

Brooks, A. & Agate, E. (1997) *Waterways and wetlands: a practical handbook.* British Trust for Conservation Volunteers, Doncaster 45-72

Bunyan, P. (1988) Safety and the school pond. *Primary Science Review* 7: 21-22

DES (1995) *Building Bulletin,* Department for Education and Science, London.

Drake, M.; Williams, P.; Biggs, J. & Whitfield, M. (1996) *Managing ponds for wildlife,* English Nature, Peterborough 3-32

Kersey, R. (1997) *Considerations when designing a pond for teaching,* Cliffe House Field Studies Centre, Huddersfield 1-5

Kirklees Metropolitan Council (1995) *School grounds development in Kirklees,* Kirklees Inspection and Monitoring Service, Huddersfield 29-38

Latham, D. (1995) The value of garden ponds for amphibian conservation. *Journal of Practical Ecology and Conservation* **1:** 24-31

Manchester Polytechnic (1977) *Ask the kids - planning the school site,* Manchester Polytechnic, Manchester

NCC (1990) *Curriculum guidance No. 7: Environmental education,* National Curriculum Council, York 7-9

Oldham, R.S. & Swan, M.J.S. (1995) Pond loss - the present position. J Biggs & C. Aistrop, *Protecting Britain's Ponds,* Pond Conservation Group 8-25

Oppenheim, A.N. (1992) *Questionnaire design, interviewing and attitude measurement.* Pinter, London 24-78

Pond Action (1994) *The Oxfordshire pond survey.* Pond Action, Oxford

Sansom, A. (1993) *Ponds and conservation: a rough guide to pond restoration,* National Rivers Authority, Leeds 7-54

Tansley, A. (1987) What is ecology? *Biological Journal of the Linnean Society,* **32:** 17-29

Williams, P.; Biggs, J.; Corfield, C.; Fox, G,; Walker, D. & Whitfield, M. (1997) Designing new ponds for wildlife. *British Wildlife* **8:** 137-150

A history of pond degradation in the East Midlands: Hermitage Pond, Mansfield, Notts

C. O. Hunt & J. Corr

Department of Geographical & Environmental Sciences, University of Huddersfield, Queensgate, Huddersfield HD1 3DH, UK.

Urban ponds can be an amenity for city dwellers, but this amenity is devalued by the degradation of the pond ecosystem. Palaeoecological techniques can offer baseline data for restoration projects, to enable sensitive and ecologically 'realistic' project design. Mansfield District Council wished to improve Hermitage Pond, Mansfield, Nottinghamshire as part of their River Maun Pathway initiative, since the pond is hypereutrophic and effectively biologically 'dead'. We describe molluscan, palynological, and sedimentary evidence for the previous state and degradation history of the pond. This early nineteenth century industrial pond was degraded by effluent from housing, a sewage farm and a chicken farm which were built in its catchment during the twentieth century, resulting in the loss of most fauna and flora.

Introduction

Urban ponds can be a major amenity for city dwellers, but it is recognised that the quality of this amenity is devalued by the degradation of the pond ecosystem (Moss, 1988, 187-188; Horne & Goldman, 1994, 7). Figures for degraded urban ponds are not easily available, but common experience suggests that a large proportion of British urban ponds are degraded. Many British water bodies have become progressively degraded through eutrophication, acidification and toxicity over the last 200 years (Moss, 1988). With the rapid growth in cities in the industrial revolution, inputs of raw sewage and toxic chemical discharges caused great, but largely unquantified damage. In the twentieth century, the construction of sewage works has somewhat mitigated the impact of raw sewage discharge and, for instance, helped in the rehabilitation of the Thames, but it is well known that effluent from sewage works can have significant impacts on aquatic ecosystems (Mason, 1961). In rural areas, runoff enriched with fertilisers and farm waste is an increasing problem. Restoration of damaged water bodies is increasingly seen as desirable (Moss, 1988, 188-197), but agencies are often less certain about what they want as the end product of the restoration process.

In order to know what the pre-degradation pond environment was, and thus what to aim for in restoration, an appraisal of the past environment may be made. Palaeoecological techniques can offer baseline data for restoration projects, to enable sensitive and ecologically 'realistic' project design. These techniques, such as mollusc analysis and diatom analysis are usually used to provide evidence of environmental change in prehistoric times (Lowe & Walker, 1984), but are equally useful for investigating the recent past. In this contribution, we describe a palaeoecological study which was done with the aim of guiding the possible restoration of an urban pond.

The Study Site

Hermitage Pond, Mansfield, Nottinghamshire (SK523598), was constructed for industrial purposes in the early nineteenth century, by damming the River Maun just downstream of the medieval King's Mill Pond. The pond is about 400 m long and up to 70 m wide, but is divided into two basins by a railway embankment. No flow figures are available, but the inlet to the pond is about 2 m wide and in low flow conditions about 0.25 m deep.

During the early years of this century, much of the catchment of the pond was developed for industry and suburban housing as Mansfield and the neighbouring town of Sutton in Ashfield sprawled. In the 1940s, a sewage works was built. This discharges into King's Mill Pond. In the early 1950s a chicken farm was built on the south side of Hermitage Pond, very close to the inlet to the pond (J. Labadz, pers. comm. 1995). Leachate from the farm is thought to reach the pond. In 1995, Mansfield District Council decided to improve Hermitage Pond as part of their River Maun Pathway Initiative. As part of the preparations for a possible wider programme of investigation, a core was taken to investigate the ecological history of the pond.

The pond can be classed as hypereutrophic and is a very severely degraded aquatic ecosystem. It is characterised by abundant plankton blooms. It has dissolved oxygen levels of 0.0-9.0 mg/l, phosphate levels of 3.6-7.6 mg/l, nitrate levels of 2.7-13.5 mg/l, conductivity figures of 878-1030 µS/cm and a pH of 7.27-7.81 (Bruce, 1996). A routine NRA survey in the inlet to the pond turned up an invertebrate assemblage characterised by large numbers of Simuliidae, *Asellus*, *Hydropsyche*, smaller numbers of *Erpobdella*, Baetidae, a few Chironomidae, Planariidae, Dendrocoelidae, Tubificidae, *Glossiphonia*, *Limnophora* and the mollusc *Lymnaea peregra* (Bruce 1996).

Sampling and Methods

Mackereth coring in the pond failed because of the 'soupy' nature of the bottom sediments, so a 50 mm piston core was taken from a marginal reed bed. This was cut into 100 mm sections and then subsampled for sediments, molluscs, algal microfossils and pollen. Subsamples for sediment analysis were weighed wet, dried and reweighed to give % water content, then ashed at 430 $^{\circ}$C and reweighed to give % carbon. Subsamples for mineral magnetic analysis were dried, ground, packed into sample containers, weighed and then analysed using a Bartington MS2B meter. Results are expressed in terms of volume susceptibility (κ). Pollen and algal microfossils were prepared using standard techniques (Hunt, 1985). Molluscs were prepared by drying and weighing the subsample, then disaggregating them in 10% hydrogen peroxide, and sieving at 0.5 mm.

Stratigraphy

The core reached a total depth of 2.25 m. In it a number of sedimentary units could be recognised (Table 1). A major discontinuity occurred around 1.45 m. Above this level, the sediments were organic muds with high water contents (70-82%) and high organic carbon percentages (19-27%), while below that depth the sediments were compact silty clays with water contents generally around 50% and carbon percentages were less than 15% (Table 1).

Table 1 Stratigraphy of the core from Hermitage Pond, Mansfield

Depth (m)	Lithology	% Water	% C	κ per g
0.00-0.75	Black highly organic mud.	70-82	30-37	0.5-3
0.75-1.45	Very dark grey organic mud, occasional shells.	72-80	19-26	2-7
1.45-1.95	Dark grey compact silty clay, shells common.	48-63	3-15	2-3
1.95-2.23	Mid grey compact silty clay, occasional shells.	46-51	4-9	1-2
2.25-2.30	Strong brown stony sandy silt.	nd	nd	nd

Palynology

The assemblages (Fig. 2: summarised in Table 2) were all sparse and poorly preserved. The appearance of modern power generation in the twentieth century is shown by the appearance of fly ash at 1.20 m. Coal mining nearby is indicated by the recycled Carboniferous spores

Table 2 Key palynological characteristics of the core from Hermitage Pond, Mansfield

Depth (m)	Land pollen	Wetland taxa	Palynofacies
0.00-0.70	Poaceae, garden plants, weeds	Cyperaceae, *Typha*, algae rare, no macrophytes	Very abundant amorphogen, recycled spores and fly ash present
0.70-1.70	Poaceae, garden plants, grassland weeds	Cyperaceae, macrophytes rare, algae common	Amorphogen and inertinite common, recycled spores common, fly ash present
1.70-2.25	Poaceae, cereals, weeds	Cyperaceae, algae and macrophytes rare	Rare inertinite and recycled spores
2.25-2.30	Poaceae, cereals, arable weeds	No aquatic macro or microflora	Rare inertinite and recycled spores

and inertinite (black inert carbon particles). The start of development in the catchment in the early years of this century is suggested by the appearance of garden plants such as *Rhododendron* and the blooming of plankton such as *Pediastrum* and *Peridinium*, which becomes marked first at 1.60 m. The plankton was most probably responding to changes in nutrient input from the catchment. Very high nutrient loading most probably led to the virtual exclusion of planktonic algae and the local extinction of macrophytes at 0.70 m. The amorphogen (amorphous organic matter) which dominates the assemblages above this point is the end product of partial decay of algae and bacteria (Batten, 1982).

Molluscs

The result of the mollusc analyses are shown in Fig. 1. A number of different assemblages can be distinguished. These can be interpreted using the work of Oklund (1964, 1969) and Macan (1977).

Assemblage A (2.23-1.95 m)
Molluscs are sparse and assemblages are of low diversity and unstable, including taxa such as *Gyraulus albus*, *Lymnaea peregra*, Sphaerids, *Pisidium amnicum*, *Valvata cristata*. These assemblages reflect a pioneer stage, with opportunist taxa like *L. peregra* and *G. albus* exploiting unstable but relatively well oxygenated and nutrient rich conditions as the pond 'settled down', after construction, but before the development of a significant macrophyte flora.

Assemblage B (1.95-1.55 m)
Molluscs are common and assemblages are stable and dominated by *Valvata cristata*. Opportunist and bottom-living taxa are rare. *V. cristata* is common in well-oxygenated, weed-filled clear waters, and this is consistent with the rarity of bottom-living and opportunist taxa.

Assemblage C (1.55-1.35 m)
Molluscs are common and assemblages are dominated by *Gyraulus albus*, with some *V. cristata*, *L. peregra* and Sphaerids. The return of the opportunist taxa (*G. albus*, *L. peregra*) and bottom fauna (Sphaerids), and the decline in importance of *V. cristata* suggests that macrophytes become less ecologically dominant and the environment more stressed, perhaps by pollution.

Assemblage D (1.35-1.05 m)
Molluscs become significantly less abundant and assemblages become unstable. *Lymnaea peregra* and *Valvata cristata* are important. Other species - *Bythinia tentaculata*, *Segmentina complanata*, *Gyraulus albus*, *Pisidium henslowanum*, Sphaerids - appear and disappear. The changing assemblages and the importance of opportunist taxa like *L. peregra* and *G. albus* points to unstable, stressed conditions with perhaps episodic pollution or other environmental stresses. The continued presence of *V. cristata* points to the existance of a macrophyte flora, while this species and *B. tentaculata*, in particular, indicate that the water body was mostly well-oxygenated.

Fig. 1 Mollusc analyses of Hermitage Pond, Mansfield (computed as numbers per kilo of wet sediment)

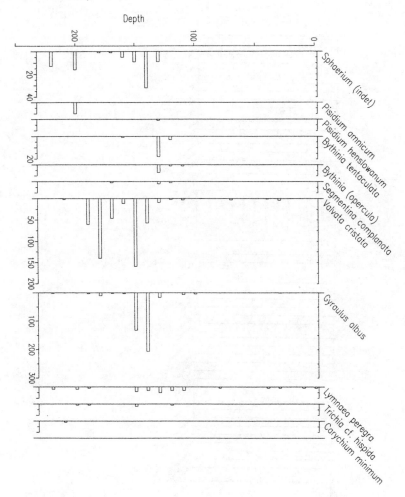

Fig. 2 Pollen and algal microfossils from Hermitage Pond, Mansfield (computed as % total pollen and spores).

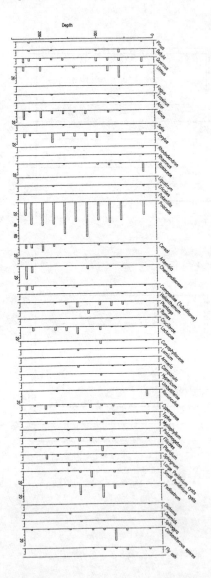

Assemblage E (1.05-0 m)
Molluscs are extremely rare. *L. peregra, V. cristata, G. albus* are occasionally present. The low incidence of aquatic molluscs points to an extremely hostile habitat. This is consistent with massive pollution, anoxic conditions and the 'death' of the pond.

The History of Hermitage Pond

The lines of evidence described above are internally consistent and allow the reconstruction of the history of Hermitage Pond. The pond was formed by the damming of the River Maun, early in the nineteenth century. The basal unit in the borehole is the old soil profile and the high counts for cereal pollen and pollen of arable weeds such as Chenopodiaceae point to a local landscape at the time being predominantly arable. After an initial stage of colonisation, indicated by small, rapidly fluctuating mollusc assemblages, the environment stabilised and pond supported a macrophyte vegetation, indicated by the mollusc population being dominated by *Valvata cristata*, a species which requires clean water and abundant water weed. Sedimentation rates were very slow.

In the early years of this century, falling cereal percentages and rises in grassland weeds indicate that arable agriculture ceased in the catchment and the construction of housing estates and the sewage works commenced. These led to increased nutrient input, which led to mild eutrophication and planktonic algal blooms, though the macrophyte flora was able to persist and the clearwater mollusc fauna was partially replaced by more tolerant taxa, including *Gyraulus albus* and *Lymnaea peregra*. The sedimentation rate rose, partly because sediment was liberated by construction activity in the catchment, and partly because of the increased organic productivity in the pond. (Morgan & Davidson [1986] quotes as much as a 7000-fold increase in sediment flux with urban construction). Eutrophication progressively worsened and the amount of organic matter produced rose. The huge quantity of organic matter led to anoxia (lack of free oxygen) in the bottom sediments, which prevented decay processes operating to completion. Consequently, the silty clay sediment were replaced by organic muds. Molluscs were severely limited towards the end of this phase, though macrophytic vegetation and algal blooms persisted.

In more recent years, most probably as leachate from the poultry farm reached the pond, eutrophication became even more severe and macrophytes, planktonic algae and molluscs were virtually eliminated. The sedimentation rate rose, partly because organic matter was not destroyed as anoxic conditions became more prevalent.

Discussion

This study was done to provide baseline data for the possible restoration of Hermitage Pond. Hermitage Pond had a dynamic history and it can be argued that its biodiversity was probably highest under conditions of moderate eutrophication - and thus pollution load. A cleaner pond might have lower biodiversity

This study thus leads to a thorny question - to what should the pond restorer aim? What point in the past is the 'ideal' for restoration? This is an important point, for in this case there was never a truly 'natural' state. as the pond is an artificial feature. The point is the same for all restoration projects, however, since environmental change and natural succession processes mean that few environments are truly stable over any but the shortest timescales. (Similarly, restoration projects, once completed, will then start to evolve, and not always in a predictable fashion!)

In the case of Hermitage Pond, the costs of restoration, particularly in sealing off the leachate from the poultry farm and in achieving stricter effluent standards on the Sewage Works, militate against the project. Nevertheless, palaeoecological methods have enabled the identification of the fauna and flora which lived in the pond in the past, and do provide a useful baseline for potential restoration.

Acknowledgements

We thank Dr J. C. Labadz for much useful information and help with visiting the site.

References
Batten, D. J. (1982) Palynofacies, palaeoenvironments and petroleum. *Journal of Micropalaeontology*, 1, 107-114.

Bruce, J. A. (1996) *Influences of human activity on water quality indicators: a case study, the Hermitage Pond,. Mansfield.* Unpublished dissertation, University of Huddersfield.

Horne, A. R & Goldman, C. R. (1994) *Limnology* (2 ed.). McGraw-Hill, New York.

Hunt, C. O. (1985) Recent advances in pollen extraction techniques: a brief review. Feiller, N. R. J., Gilbertson, D. D. & Ralph, N. G. A. (eds.) *Palaeobiological investigations: research design, methods and data analysis.* British Archaeological Reports, Oxford, International Series, 266, 181-188.

Lowe, J. J. & Walker, M. J. C. (1984) *Reconstructing Quaternary Environments.* Longman, London.

Macan, T. T. (1977) *A key to the British fresh- and brackish-water gastropods.* Freshwater Biological Association, Ambleside.

Mason, C. F. (1981) *Biology of freshwater pollution.* Longman, London.

Morgan, R. P. C. & Davidson, D. A. (1986) *Soil erosion and conservation.* Longman, London.

Moss, B. (1988) *Ecology of fresh waters, man and medium.* (2 ed.) Blackwell, Oxford.

Oklund, J. (1964) The eutrophic Lake Borrevan (Norway): an ecological study on shore and bottom fauna with special reference to gastropods. *Folia Limnologica Scandinavia*, 13, 1-337.

Oklund, J. (1969) Distribution and ecology of the freshwater snails of Norway. *Malacologia*, 9 143-151.

Theme II:

Ecological status of ponds

Biodiversity in the ponds of lowland North-west England

J.P.Guest

Jonathan Guest Ecological Survey
47 Marlston Avenue, Chester, CH4 8HE

Abstract

During the summers of 1995 and 1996 492 ponds in lowland
North-west England were surveyed in the first two seasons of the
Pond*Life* **Critical Biodiversity Survey**. Most of these ponds are
former marl-pits, with smaller numbers of brick-pits, oxbows and
industrial ponds. Some 244 plant and 278 macroinvertebrate taxa
have been identified. The presence of amphibians and birds was
also recorded.

An overview is presented of the types of ponds encountered.
The relevance of these pond types to nature conservation is
discussed briefly.

Introduction

During the summers of 1995 and 1996 492 ponds in lowland North-west England
were surveyed for the Pond*Life* **Critical Biodiversity Survey**. The great majority of these
ponds are former marl-pits, with smaller numbers of brick-pits, oxbows and industrial ponds.
239 of these ponds lie in Cheshire, 10 in Wirral, 208 in Lancashire and 35 in Greater
Manchester.

All plants (including charophytes) rooted below the winter high water mark were
recorded. Evidence of presence of amphibians was sought by netting, searching for eggs, and
by noting any animals on land beside the ponds. Macroinvertebrates recorded included
molluscs, beetles, bugs, dragonflies, mayflies, caddis and a few smaller groups. Birds were
noted as was the presence of fish.

Plants

Some 244 plant taxa were found, including about 23 introduced species. The status of
plant species in the region is well known, with regional floras starting from the last century.
There have been a few surprises however, with e.g. records of Soft Hornwort (*Ceratophyllum
submersum*), Alternate Water-milfoil (*Myriophyllum alterniflorum*) and the nationally scarce
Cowbane (*Cicuta virosa* - 19 Cheshire records). Cowbane leaves are sometimes used by
Great Crested Newts (*Triturus cristatus*) to wrap their eggs.

Spiked Water-milfoil (*Myriophyllum spicatum*) and Pond Water-crowfoot (*Ranunculus peltatus*) are characteristic of ecological mitigation ponds, and occur only rarely in old established settings. Ten of 15 records of the milfoil and 7 of 13 records of the crowfoot are evident introductions. Least Duckweed (*Lemna minuta*) and New Zealand Pigmyweed (*Crassula helmsii*) are thinly scattered usually in ponds accessible to the general public, but the duckweed is spreading also into remote farmland ponds.

The region lies at the edge of the range of certain types of duckweed vegetation. Fat Duckweed (*Lemna gibba*) was found four times to south and once to north of the Mersey; Great Duckweed (*Spirodela polyrhiza*) 13 times to the south and four to the north; the aquatic liverwort *Riccia fluitans* 12 times to south and 5 times to the north; and *Ricciocarpos natans* in five ponds all to south of the Mersey.

Swamp plants

Rodwell (1991, 1995) lists potential swamp dominants found in British plant communities. Occurrences of these potential dominants during the survey are summarised in Table 2. Presence of such a species in a pond does not necessarily signify dominance. There again, it is common to find stands of two or more dominants in different parts of a pond.

Branched Bur-reed (*Sparganium erectum*), Greater Reedmace (*Typha latifolia*), Reed Canary-grass (*Phalaris arundinacea*) and Water Horsetail (*Equisetum fluviatile*) are the most usual dominants. Floating Sweet-grass (*Glyceria fluitans*), Common Spike-rush (*Eleocharis palustris*) and Cyperus Sedge (*Carex pseudocyperus*) occur very commonly, but only the sweet-grass is at all frequent as a dominant. Rarely, Plicate Sweet-grass (*Glyceria notata*) was found as a dominant, especially where there is a slight movement of water through a pond. Yellow Flag (*Iris pseudacorus*) also occurs dominates in species-poor or clean stands.

Greater Reedmace was frequently found as floating mats which, according to Rodwell (1995; 185) were not encountered during the preparation of the National Vegetation Classification (NVC). Reed Canary-grass was found as floating mats and emergent stands in what were permanent pools even during the drought of 1995 and 1996. This conflicts with the habitat summary for the species in Rodwell (1995).

Rush-pasture plants

The typical rush-pasture fringe to a north-west English marl-pit has Creeping Bent (*Agrostis stolonifera*), Yorkshire Fog (*Holcus lanatus*), Creeping Buttercup (*Ranunculus repens*) and Soft Rush (*Juncus effusus*) or Hard Rush (*J. inflexus*). These are of course the constant species in the MG10 *Juncus - Holcus* rush-pasture of the NVC (Rodwell 1992). The fringes of marl-pits form an important refuge for rush-pasture species which in many cases have otherwise vanished from whole farms (Table 3).

Typical field-ponds in the region have a limited aquatic flora; more or less dense swamp vegetation; and a marginal fringe of rush-pasture, usually less than a metre in width. This fringe is the only surviving remnant in many parishes of what was once a common habitat in the region.

Aquatic plants

The scarcity of submerged aquatic plants came as something of a surprise. Only 86 ponds (17%) held any submerged Pondweed (*Potamogeton*) species for example, whereas Broad-leaved Pondweed (*P. natans*), with floating leaves, was found in 168 ponds (34%).

A particularly high proportion of alien species was found amongst the aquatics, plants being introduced for ornament; as oxygenators for fish; or by accident. Certain "native" species are often associated with what are obviously introduced species and may share this origin. Rigid Hornwort (*Ceratophyllum demersum*), for example, is often sold by aquarists. In twelve out of 18 ponds in which it occurred it was accompanied by pet-shop species such as Nuttall's Waterweed (*Elodea nuttallii*), Canadian Waterweed (*E. canadensis*) or Curly Water-thyme (*Lagarosiphon major*).

Table 1   Alien and commonly introduced aquatic plants found in 492 lowland ponds in North-western England

	No. of ponds (out of 492)	% of ponds
Alien species:		
Elodea canadensis	51	10.37
Elodea nuttallii	32	6.50
Nymphaea spp./var.	8	1.63
Lagarosiphon major	6	1.22
Crassula helmsii	5	1.02
Lemna minuta	5	1.02
Azolla filiculoides	1	0.20
Myriophyllum aquaticum	1	0.20
Introduced "natives":		
Ceratophyllum demersum	18	3.66
Myriophyllum spicatum	15	3.05
Ranunculus peltatus	13	2.64
Stratiotes aloides	10	2.03
Nymphoides peltata	5	1.02

Table 2 Occurrences of potential swamp dominants (after Rodwell 1991, 1995) in 492 ponds in north-western England.

	No. of ponds (out of 492)	% of ponds
Sparganium erectum	234	47.56
Glyceria fluitans	216	43.90
Phalaris arundinacea	169	34.35
Typha latifolia	142	28.86
Equisetum fluviatile	107	21.75
Eleocharis palustris	97	19.72
Carex pseudocyperus	94	19.11
Carex otrubae	25	5.08
Typha angustifolia	21	4.27
Phragmites australis	17	3.46
Carex acutiformis	15	3.05
Carex rostrata	14	2.85
Carex paniculata	13	2.64
Acorus calamus	10	2.03
Scirpus l. lacustris	8	1.63
Glyceria maxima	6	1.22
Scirpus l. tabernaemontani	3	0.61
Carex elata	1	0.20
Carex riparia	1	0.20
Carex vesicaria	1	0.20
Scirpus maritimus	1	0.20
Salix cinerea	210	42.68
Alnus glutinosa	93	18.90
Salix fragilis	73	14.84

Amphibians

Most of the fieldwork was done between late May and July, too late to find frog spawn for example; and a single visit only was made to each pond. There is little doubt that earlier visits would have found more Frog (*Rana temporaria*) and Toad (*Bufo bufo*) presence: in quite a number of ponds only single or nearly solitary tadpoles were found, showing that the species had almost been missed.

Table 3   Occurrences of selected rush-pasture species around the fringes of 492 ponds in North-western England

	No. of ponds	% of ponds
Holcus lanatus	392	79.67
Juncus effusus	378	76.83
Ranunculus repens	340	69.11
Agrostis stolonifera	307	62.40
Juncus inflexus	194	39.43
Cardamine pratensis	160	32.52
Lotus pedunculatus	63	12.80
Myosotis scorpioides	29	5.89
Filipendula ulmaria	27	5.49
Lychnis flos-cuculi	27	5.49

Table 4 Occurrences of amphibian species by ponds in North-western England during the first two years of the survey.

	North of Mersey		South of Mersey		Total	
No. of ponds surveyed:	243		244		487	
Ponds containing:						
Great Crested Newt	36	15%	90	37%	126	26%
Palmate Newt	12	5%	1	.004%	13	3%
Smooth Newt	55	23%	47	19%	102	21%
Ordinary Newt	51	21%	51	21%	102	21%
Smooth + Ord. Newt	106	44%	98	40%	204	42%
Frog	90	37%	100	41%	190	39%
Toad	44	18%	65	27%	109	22%

Even so, the survey has shown that the Great Crested Newt is widely distributed, even common, across much of the region. It is questionable whether any suitable ponds in Cheshire lack the species. Conversely the scarcity of lowland Palmate Newts (*Triturus helveticus*)

south of the Mersey is remarkable. Table 4 summarises recorded occurrences of amphibian species during the two years of the survey. "Ordinary newts" are eggs and/or larvae of Smooth or Palmate Newts in the absence of adults.

133 ponds (27%) were found to hold just one amphibian species and another 133 to hold two species. 65 (13%) held three species; 11 (2%) held four species and just one pond held five species. The number of amphibian species present in a pond is only one of many criteria that can be used to evaluate a pond for nature conservation. If we take the narrow criterion that a pond with five amphibian species is better than one with four, then all the ponds across much of lowland Cheshire and parts of Lancashire will automatically be second rate because of such immutable factors as geology and geographical location. The Palmate Newt is largely confined within the region to ponds on the coal measures and on heathland. The geographical area within which five amphibian species are likely to occur together is therefore limited. Lowland ponds on boulder clay have other attributes and cannot be compared directly with ponds on the shales.

Invertebrates

Amongst the invertebrates, there are problems of definition as to what constitutes a wetland species. The scope of the survey has widened with increasing experience to include Scirtid beetles, whose larvae are aquatic, and to leaf beetles associated with wetland plants. There are molluscs, such as *Carychium minimum* and *Euconulus alderi*, that live in flushes in woodland and elsewhere and which are not strictly pond creatures, but then neither are stoneflies such as *Nemurella picteti* or ladybirds such as *Anisosticta 19-punctata*. There are others, such as the many ground beetles, spiders and others which live on dense vegetation rafts, that are not yet included. The slug *Deroceras laeve* is commonly netted submerged in grass mats, but has not been consistently recorded. It is important to remember that aquatic and terrestrial habitats run into one another, and that this boundary zone is in many ways more complex than either open water or many terrestrial habitats. Table 5 summarises invertebrates recorded by the end of the 1996 season.

In elaborating on these results, it is useful to take a holistic approach and describe the types of ponds encountered, rather than to think in terms of amphibian ponds, beetle ponds or dragonfly ponds. **Ponds have to be viewed as complex habitats with multiple layers of interest**. A particular problem where pond conservation is concerned is ignorance amongst nature conservation advisers of the diversity of ponds as habitats for flora and especially fauna. Various types of ponds should be recognised. The following notes concentrate on marl-pit ponds. Bog pools and some other types of ponds will fit badly into the sequence.

Table 5 Invertebrate groups recorded during a survey of 492 ponds in north-western England.

Tricladida (flatworms)   222 records
  5 taxa   (*Polycelis niger/tenuis* and *Dugesia lugubris/polychroa*
                              not separated)
Hirudinea (leeches)   551 records
  9 species
Mollusca (snails, mussels etc.)   1560 records
  29 taxa   (including *Oxyloma pfeifferi* and aggregated *Pisidium* but
                              excluding such semi-terrestrials as *Carychium minimum*
                              and *Euconulus alderi*)
  1 Red Data Book category 2 species
Araneae (spiders)   10 records
  1 species
Malacostraca (shrimps and hoglice)   546 records
  4 species
Ephemeroptera (mayflies)   264 records
  7 species
Plecoptera (stoneflies)   10 records
  2 species
Megaloptera (alderflies)   114 records
  1 species
Odonata (dragonflies and damselflies)   732 records
  15 species
Hemiptera (bugs)   2178 records
  36 species
Lepidoptera (china-mark moths)   96 records
  4 species
Trichoptera (caddis)   481 records
  26 species
Coleoptera (beetles)   5713 records
  139 species
  1 Red Data Book category 1 species
  1 Nationally Notable (Na) species
  26 Nationally Notable (Nb) species

Types of ponds

Field ponds in north-western England, by and large, fit somewhere along a successional line. When first dug, or following dredging, they have high pH values following the release of bases from the clay. [The result will be similar whether the pond is dredged in two halves in successive years, or all at once.] Newly dredged ponds attract a suite of characteristic species, including e.g. stoneworts (*Chara* spp.), certain *Haliplus* beetles, the nationally scarce scavenger beetle *Enochrus melanocephalus*, and Emperor (*Anax imperator*) and Broad-bodied Chaser (*Libellula depressa*) dragonflies. Some of these species are encountered in only a tiny percentage of ponds, but they quickly find their way into newly suitable waters. New ponds are always to be welcomed, but their fauna is highly mobile and probably does not need special protection.

There is a large body of mostly common species which live in mid-succession ponds where for example *Sparganium erectum* or *Typha latifolia* form fringing swamps. This is the largest group of ponds, and one from which it is harder to select individual ponds for special protection. Larger, deeper ponds contain species which may be common in lakes, such as the whirligig *Gyrinus marinus* and the Red-eyed Damselfly (*Erythromma najas*). A literature search and perhaps fieldwork need to be undertaken to clarify this. Many a Toad pond of course is large and deep.

One special type of mid-succession pond, thinly scattered across the dairying and cattle country of Cheshire and Lancashire, is the "bug pond". These are ponds into which cattle wade. The resultant fouling leads to a vigorous growth of algae and flourishing populations of corixids (water boatmen) including *Sigara concinna*, a species equally characteristic of flashes resulting from salt extraction. The nationally scarce great diving beetle *Dytiscus circumflexus* is typical of bug ponds and also of saltworks flashes. The tiny scavenger beetle *Ochthebius viridis* (also scarce), found last year for the first time in the region in a Cheshire bug-pond, is also said to frequent brackish pools. It becomes difficult to separate the brackish conditions of the Cheshire salt-field from the effects of cow muck. Such plants as Spear-leaved Orache (*Atriplex prostrata*) and Red Goosefoot (*Chenopodium rubrum*) are common to both habitats.

In late succession, ponds become more extreme in their characteristics and provide shelter for uncommon species. A large proportion becomes colonised by Common Sallow (*Salix cinerea*) which ultimately casts heavy shade. On some farms these thickets are the only scrub available for, or at least form an important component of the territories of Reed Buntings (*Emberiza schoeniclus*), Lesser Whitethroats (*Sylvia curruca*) or Willow Warblers (*Phylloscopus trochilus*). Ponds with dappled shade may contain breeding Great Crested Newts and surprising numbers of invertebrates. In other cases, miniature stands of Alder (*Alnus glutinosa*) woodland form over Tussock Sedge (*Carex paniculata*) or Lesser Pond Sedge (*Carex acutiformis*). These are worthy of conservation in their own right for their ornithological and invertebrate interest.

More interesting for aquatic invertebrates however are those late succession ponds which have remained free from scrub or trees. These are the ponds most in need of protection, which is generally the opposite of intervention. **It has to be recognised that botanically dull ponds are often important invertebrate or amphibian habitats.** Ponds with mats of floating grasses, especially where the water level fluctuates seasonally, may contain once common molluscs such as *Anisus leucostoma, Planorbis planorbis* or *Aplexa hypnorum* (Table 6). The Red Data Book snail *Lymnaea glabra* and the Cheshire breeding populations of *Hydrochara caraboides* have been found in such grass mats (Guest 1996).

Seasonal ponds (like rush-pastures) are victims of the trend towards landscape simplification, being particularly vulnerable to in-filling or dredging.

Floating rafts of *Typha latifolia* may be very rich in faunal terms, with scarce scavenger beetles (e.g. *Cercyon* species), water ladybirds (*Anisosticta 19-punctata*), unusual hoverflies (*Anasimyia* spp.) and a rich fauna of terrestrial invertebrates. Great Crested Newts often breed successfully in small pools at the edge of the rafts, kept open by the cutting hooves of cattle. In winter Jack Snipe (*Lymnocryptes minimus*) crouch amongst the flattened vegetation. Unshaded, late succession ponds should have priority for conservation. Dredging is seldom appropriate.

Table 6 Occurrence of molluscs typical of shallow, grassy pools during the survey of 492 ponds in North-western England.

No. of records:	south of Mersey	north of Mersey	Total	% of ponds with presence
Anisus leucostoma	4	16	20	4.07
Aplexa hypnorum	5	6	11	2.24
Bathyomphalus contortus	16	9	25	5.08
Lymnaea glabra	-	2	2	0.41
Lymnaea truncatula	3	14	17	3.46
Planorbis planorbis	5	3	8	1.63

Pond Conservation

More than 30% of ponds surveyed held at least one species classed as Regionally Notable, Nationally Notable or rarer. Of 281 invertebrate taxa recorded, 131 (47%) were found in 2% or less of ponds and only 33 (12%) in 20% or more of ponds. Some seemingly uncommon species occur more commonly in other habitats or at other seasons, but it appears that many are genuinely restricted to a small number of ponds in the region. There are, therefore, far too many valuable ponds for the small number of professional and volunteer conservationists ever to dream of managing effectively, and yet we cannot continue to lose or mismanage ponds without losing species. We have to work with land owners and managers to ensure that as many as possible of these ponds are safeguarded.

When local authorities or conservation bodies ask for advice on how to select ponds to safeguard, they are given a wide and confusing variety of answers depending on the yardstick used for assessment. The botanists will have their preferences, the odonatists theirs, the coleopterists theirs, and so on. When it comes to evaluation, any pond should be assessed against a bundle of yardsticks. The broad successional sequence outlined above gives a framework into which most species of particular nature conservation interest can be fitted.

A lot of work remains to be done to analyse the data gained in the first two years of the survey. A third season of fieldwork has produced much additional information from 250 additional ponds. A final round of survey is planned for 1998.

Acknowledgment

I wish to acknowledge the cooperation of David Bentley in the survey and indirectly in the preparation of this paper. David operates as a specialist pond and amphibian consultant and can be contacted at 11 Wolsey Street, Radcliffe, M26 3AS.

References:

Guest, J.P. (1996) Hydrochara caraboides *L. in Cheshire*, unpublished report for English Nature.

Rodwell, J.S. (1991, Ed.) *British Plant Communities, Volume 1: Woodlands and scrub*, Cambridge University Press.

Rodwell, J.S. (1992, Ed.) *British Plant Communities, Volume 3: Grasslands and montane communities*, Cambridge University Press.

Rodwell, J.S. (1995, Ed.) *British Plant Communities, Volume 5: Swamps and aquatic communities*, Cambridge University Press.

The role of ponds in biodiversity objectives - a case study on Merseyside

C.M. Bennett

Joint Countryside Advisory Service, Bryant House, Liverpool Road North,
Maghull, Merseyside L31 2PA, UK

Abstract

Biological data on plants and animals were recorded from ponds in an agricultural area in Knowsley, Merseyside. These data were examined to determine a) presence or absence of species of UK, sub-regional and local conservation concern, b) distribution of plants and animals across survey area, and c) relationship with distribution, age and abundance of ponds. Recommendations are made relating species of conservation concern and pond habitats to developing Local Biodiversity Action Plans within Merseyside.

Introduction

The biological diversity of ponds within north Merseyside has been little studied. Studies which have been carried out (Young & Williams, 1991; Lowther, 1984) have been limited by being closely dependent on 1) species which are of national or international importance such as natterjack toads (*Bufo calamita*) or great-crested newt (*Triturus cristatus*), 2) specific sites in relation to management or development or 3) protection of landscape features. The importance of the biological resource as a whole within ponds has not been examined in north Merseyside. The loss of ponds and their biological resources has been raised as an issue by several organisations and individuals and was demonstrated nationally in the Countryside Survey of 1984 (Barr, C. J. *et al.*, 1991; Biggs *et al.*, 1994). Ponds have been proposed as ancient natural habitats, particularly those which are natural in origin, and continuity of existence in an area is of paramount importance in conserving wetland biodiversity (Biggs *et al.*, 1994).

Site Description

A sample area was defined in the district of Knowsley, Merseyside. This sample area was based on the route corridor examined in connection with the development of A5300 Knowsley Expressway. The area is approximately 1 km (east to west) by 5 km (north to south). All 38 ponds fall within the rectangle defined by grid references SJ.470840 (southwest corner) and SJ.470900 (northeast corner). Each of the 38 ponds was present at time of survey.

The land has been in agricultural use for several hundred years, and is currently in arable farming. Much of the land is Grade 1 and 2 in the agricultural land use classification and so is highly productive and valued by the farming community. The area is also part of the Merseyside Green Belt and separates the urban areas of Netherley and Halewood in Merseyside from Widnes in Cheshire. The area forms part of the Ditton catchment and is largely drained by a combination of ditches and pumped drainage systems (Anon, 1997). The landscape has been recognised as comprising features of significant landscape interest within its gently rolling landform (Anon, 1993a).

Methodology

Survival and minimum age of each pond was established from a combination of the 1st Edition Ordnance Survey map (1848) and time-series aerial photography (1945, 1961, 1975, 1984, 1989, 1993, 1995).

Biological data on ponds in the sample area were available from 1) Phase 1 Habitat Survey of Knowsley, 1981; 2) faunal surveys (1991) undertaken in connection with A5300 Knowsley Expressway, (each pond contained water at the time of survey); 3) faunal and lower plant data collated as part of the Knowsley Nature Conservation Audit in 1996 and 4) Phase 2 Site Survey reports.

Distribution of groups of invertebrates within ponds in the sample area were recorded. Species of UK conservation concern were identified from those listed in the UK Biodiversity Steering Group Report's short, medium and long lists. Sub-regionally and locally important plant species were identified from the Sites/Species Databases for Knowsley, St Helens and Sefton.

Results

Pond Age

The ponds examined are among some of the oldest habitats remaining in the district of Knowsley. All ponds, except two, are present on the 1st edition Ordnance Survey map. This provides an approximate date of 1848. All 38 ponds are present on the earliest aerial photography of 1945. Minimum pond age thus varies from over 50 years to, for the great majority, over 150 years.

Examination of time-series aerial photography from 1945 to 1995 surprisingly shows that all 38 ponds have survived throughout the period, with all ponds readily recognisable since 1945 on each set of photography. Water was found by survey to be present in all ponds in 1991 (Young & Williams, 1991) although it has not been possible to check for continued presence of water in all ponds since then. Some ponds have remained in the open agricultural landscape. However, examination of sequential aerial photography shows that some ponds have become surrounded by trees and scrub and on 1993 and 1995 aerial photography existence of some ponds is difficult, but not impossible, to discern.

Biological Data

Distribution of data

There are 20 groups recorded comprising plants, amphibians, birds, mosses and liverworts, fish, fungi, mammals and 13 groups of invertebrates. Only 11 out of 38 ponds have plant data (28.9%). All ponds have invertebrate data though no ponds have representatives of each group. Most of the other animal groups are poorly represented. For example, unexpectedly, there is no specific survey information on amphibians.

Invertebrate data are most widespread in this sample area, although this is not indicative of the situation in the remainder of Knowsley. From the sample area, there are records from the following groups: Annelida, Arachnida, Coelentera, Coleoptera, Crustacea, Diptera, Ephemeroptera, Hemiptera, Mollusca, Nematoda, Odonata, Platyhelminthes, and Trichoptera. Analysis of the distribution of these invertebrate data clearly shows that the number of groups and taxa recorded per pond varies considerably. No ponds have records from all 13 invertebrate groups, with a range of 10 groups (Pond 7) to one group (Pond 9).

Distribution of invertebrates

The frequency of number of groups of invertebrates per pond is shown in Figure 1, and distribution of groups of invertebrates in ponds is set out in Table 1.

As can be seen, most ponds have between five and seven groups of invertebrates. Two groups were not identified to genus or species level (Nematoda and Hydracarina). Species were not determined for the following genera: Pisidium, Cyclopoida, Colymbetinae, Hydroporinae, Dytiscidae, Helodidae, Aedes, Chironomini, Tanypodinae, Tanytarsini, and Orthocladinae.

Figure 1 Frequency of number of groups of invertebrates per pond

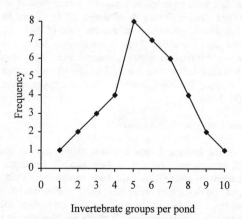

Invertebrate groups per pond

The most common invertebrate groups recorded are Annelids (34 ponds, 89.5%), followed by Crustacea and Diptera (32 ponds, 84.2%). Nematodes were the least recorded group, present in only one pond (2.6%).

Table 1 Distribution of groups of invertebrates in ponds

Group	Sites (no.)	Specific ponds
Annelids	34	1-10, 12-33, 35-36
Arachnida	8	1, 10, 13, 18, 27-29, 37
Coelentera	4	12-13, 27, 36
Coleoptera	26	3, 7, 10-21, 23-24, 26-30, 32-34, 37-38
Crustacea	32	1-8, 10-21, 23-32, 34, 37
Diptera	32	1-2, 4-8, 10-15, 17-23, 25, 27-28, 30-38
Ephemeroptera	9	7-8, 14-16, 20-21, 23, 26
Hemiptera	14	7, 10-15, 18, 23, 27, 29-31, 34
Mollusca	25	1-3, 6-8, 10, 13, 15-24, 26-27, 29, 32-33, 36-37
Nematoda	1	34
Odonata	10	3, 6-8, 14, 18, 24, 26, 28-29
Platyhelminthes	11	1-2, 7, 13, 17, 20, 24-27, 36
Trichoptera	8	6-8, 12, 14-16, 20

Most of the invertebrate data were recorded in a specific survey looking at aquatic invertebrates in ponds, ditches and streams (Young & Williams, 1991). From 38 ponds, 92 taxa were recorded, providing an average number of taxa per pond of 2.42. The range of taxa per pond recorded varied from one to 30. Thus, it can be seen that no pond holds more than 32.6% (30 taxa per pond) of the taxa within the sample area. Also, distribution of taxa in ponds is variable. It is important to note that 28 taxa (30.4%) are recorded from only one pond and are hence at risk. The most commonly recorded taxon is Cyclopoida which is present in 28 ponds (73.7%).

Species of UK, sub-regional and local conservation concern

Thorough examination of the biological data available shows that no species of conservation concern in a UK context were present in these ponds. However, several species with restricted distributions in Merseyside have been recognised. Plant species with a restricted distribution in Knowsley are recorded from Pond 8 (nine species, seven of which are wetland species) and Pond 29 (six species, five of which are wetland species), a total of 12 locally rare plant species. Eight of these 12 plants are also rare in the sub-region of north Merseyside (Knowsley, St. Helens and Sefton). These are *Bidens cernua*, *Callitriche palustris*, *Carex acutiformis*, *Potamogeton crispus*, *Potamogeton polygonifolius*,

Ranunculus peltatus, *Stellaria palustris*, and *Veronica anagallis-aquatica*. None of these is a nationally rare or nationally scarce plant.

There are insufficient invertebrate data available to identify local or sub-regional distributions at present. However, the finding that many invertebrate species were recorded from only one pond during the course of the survey has considerable implications for biodiversity conservation in Knowsley.

Discussion

Pond Age

The finding that no ponds in this area have been lost by either destruction or natural succession over the last 150 years is surprising, especially as considerable numbers have been destroyed in immediately adjacent farmland. Biggs *et al.* (1994) describe ponds as "ancient natural habitats" and refer to the different ages of ponds having different but often equal nature conservation value. The ponds examined in this study are, with exception of only two, greater than 150 years in age. The management techniques used over that period of time are unknown. However, it can be assumed that management of ponds may have taken place at irregular intervals over the last 150 years, particularly as these ponds contained water up to 1991. It is possible that the digging of pits for marl has occurred in this part of Knowsley from around the beginning of the post-medieval period (Cleaver, 1982). Given the length of time the ponds have been present, it would be expected that the biological resources contained within them would be significant. The above results demonstrate that the biological resources, particularly of plants, within this sample area are significant not only to the district of Knowsley but also to the sub-region.

Biological Resources

Both Biggs *et al.* (1994) and Williams *et al.* (1997) have described the variations in plant and animal communities that occur in ponds of different ages. They highlight that most invertebrate populations are highly mobile and may often be found in newly excavated ponds within a few years, provided there is a suitable existing donor site nearby. Given the distribution of invertebrates in the sample area, with no pond containing more than 32.6% of the invertebrates resource, it is clear that the impact from loss of even one pond and its communities would result in a significant loss of the biological resource within the district and possibly the sub-region. Although data are incomplete for other groups, plant resources would also be significantly affected by loss of certain ponds and it is expected that this pattern would be followed within the other groups.

Animal communities within the sample ponds vary in their complexity, as described by the number of taxa per pond. Although no data are available to describe the reasons for such variability in this study, Biggs *et al.* (1994) and Williams *et al.* (1997) refer to the characteristics which affect pond communities. These can be summarised as water quality, location, pond-mosaics, water depth and fluctuation, bare mud, management and succession. It is clear from the invertebrate communities present that at least some of these factors are operative within the sample area. Hence, each pond has its own physical and biotic characteristics which are not reproduced elsewhere within the study area. The value of each pond is significant in its own right, but as part of a complex within a relatively small area of 5 km², each pond contributes to a significant biodiversity resource within the study area.

Biodiversity Implications

Conservation of biodiversity is now attracting significant resource allocations within the UK. These changes result from the UK Government signing the Convention on Biological Diversity in 1992 at Rio. Since then, the UK Government has published its Biodiversity Action Plan (Anon, 1994) and also recommended the preparation and implementation of local Biodiversity Action Plans as a means to secure biodiversity conservation. It is now recognised and accepted that conserving biodiversity depends equally as much on conserving the wider countryside as on conserving statutorily protected sites (SSSIs etc.) This recognition is the driving force behind English Nature's Natural Areas programme (Anon, 1993b).

Ponds were not recorded in the Countryside Survey 1990, although they were recorded in the Countryside Survey 1984. Pond losses and gains nationally are very difficult to quantify and hence the loss or gain of pond biodiversity is at present impossible to estimate with reliability. The UK Biodiversity Steering Group Report does refer to ponds within its Standing Open Water Habitat Statement, yet makes few specific recommendations for ponds.

Regionally, a Biodiversity Steering Group has been established in the north west and a regional biodiversity audit is being carried out. This audit will set the regional framework for species and habitat action plans to be prepared and implemented, such as ponds, at the appropriate local level.

It has been demonstrated clearly that the ponds in this sample area of Knowsley contain a significant biodiversity resource for invertebrates and plants. Other groups will form part of that resource when information is available and assessed. Pond losses may occur through changes in vegetation and animal communities by deterioration in water quality and natural succession. However, the loss of any one pond by destruction needs to be avoided.

It is clear that ponds as holders of biodiversity resources within the UK have been significantly underestimated, if not at times ignored, by those agencies charged with protecting nature conservation compared to habitats that are accepted as being holders of the biodiversity resource such as ancient semi-natural woodlands, heathlands, estuaries and sand dunes. Hence, the commitments made in the UK Biodiversity Action Plan to conserving biodiversity in the wider countryside.

The following recommendations are made to aid in conserving biological diversity within the study area.

Recommendations

1. To further conservation of biodiversity in ponds on Merseyside, additional surveys of animal groups and communities are required. Specifically, survey should be targeted on amphibians, molluscs, beetles and annelids.

2. Farmers and landowners should be encouraged to retain existing ponds and create new ponds and other wetland features to ensure long-term retention of existing biodiversity. Directing land managers (farmers and other land owners) towards available grant mechanisms such as Countryside Stewardship administered by the Ministry of Agriculture, Food and Fisheries (MAFF) and Knowsley's own Landscape Improvement Grants should help to provide funding for survey and management.

3. Mersey Forest objectives and targets should include pond creation as part of the forest mosaic of habitats. As part of the Mersey Forest creation, a mosaic of habitats and land uses in woodland setting, specific targets for pond survey, retention and, if necessary, management must be set. At present, records of only creation and management are made.

4. Grant-aid for survey of existing ponds, creation of new ponds and, where appropriate, their management should be secured through existing initiatives, such as the Mersey Forest and Countryside Stewardship. MAFF looks towards additional benefits of Countryside Stewardship schemes such as whole farm plans, whereas, initially, land managers are more willing to accept small schemes and build on those.

5. Survey of ponds should be restored to the Countryside Survey which is due to take place in 1998. Analysis should examine changes between 1984 and 1998 and the results used to amend grant regimes where necessary.

6. A Pond Habitat Action Plan for Merseyside should be prepared and implemented to ensure that biodiversity resources are conserved within the wider countryside.

References

Anon. (1994) *Biodiversity. The UK Action Plan. Command 2428*, HMSO: London.

Anon. (1995) *Biodiversity: UK Steering Group Report. Volumes 1 and 2*, HMSO: London.

Barr, C.J.; Bunce, R.G.H.; Clarke, R.T.; Fuller, R.M.; Furse, M.T.; Gillespie, M.K.; Groom, G.B.; Hallam, C.J.; Hornung, M.; Howard, D.C. & Ness, M.J. (1993) *Countryside Survey 1990. Main Report.* Department of the Environment: London.

Biggs, J.; Corfield, A.; Walker, D.; Whitfield, M. & Williams, P. (1994) New approaches to the management of ponds. *British Wildlife* **5**: 273-287.

Cleaver, M. (1982) Medieval and Post-medieval Industries of Knowsley District Borough: An Introductory Outline. R.W. Cowell (Ed.) *Knowsley Rural Fringes Survey Report*, Merseyside County Council/Merseyside County Museums: Liverpool 56-65.

English Nature (1993) *Natural areas. English Nature's approach to setting nature conservation objectives*, English Nature: Peterborough.

The Environment Agency (1997) *Lower Mersey Local Environment Action Plan*, The Environment Agency: Warrington.

Knowsley MBC (1993) *Deposit Draft Unitary Development Plan Parts 1 and 2*, Knowsley Metropolitan Borough Council: Huyton.

Lowther, N. J. (1984) *Marlpits - a declining resource?* Unpublished MSc dissertation, Wye College, University of London.

Williams, P.; Biggs, J.; Corfield, A.; Fox, G.; Walker, D. & Whitfield, M. (1997) Designing new ponds for wildlife. *British Wildlife* 8: 137-150.

Young, J.O. & Williams, T.R. (1991) Aquatic Invertebrate Survey. C.M. Bennett (Ed.) *Knowsley Faunal Surveys, M57/A563 Link Road, June 1991*, unpublished report to Knowsley MBC.

Theme III:

Pond landscape change: habitat and species perspectives

The development of pond communities; chance versus predictability

M.J. Jeffries.

Division of Geography and Environmental Management, Lipman Building, University of Northumbria, Newcastle upon Tyne, NE1 8ST.

Abstract.

Adjacent ponds often support strikingly different communities. General rules describing patterns of pond-life are surprisingly difficult to pin down despite the gut feeling that ponds should fit many of the classical ecological patterns. Reliable patterns show up at national and intimate scales but medium-scale patterns e.g. consistency within a region or year to year are less predictable.

An appeal to chance processes to explain such variations has a long standing place in the literature on ponds. Chance has been used to describe at least four different phenomena; rare events, common but unpredictable colonisations, development of communities contingent on past events and chaotic dynamics. The result is that, chance influences the genetic, taxonomic and ecological biodiversity of ponds.

The impact of chance may thwart conservation which often requires predictable outcomes as management objectives. However the diversity and unpredictability of pond ecosystems is one of their intrinsic characteristics. The impact of chance is mediated by the wider landscape. Each pond is potentially unique.

Introduction.

Ecology concentrates on the search for reliable, general patterns and their causes in nature. Ecological studies of ponds are no exception, typically comparing the richness, abundance and combinations of species with likely causal factors such as pond age, area or water physicochemistry. Reviewing factors controlling faunal and floral diversity Friday (1987) distinguishes two broad categories; biogeographical (pond age, isolation and area) and habitat characteristics (habitat diversity, interactions between species, water chemistry). Friday cites repeated results of pond surveys to show correlations between species numbers and pond isolation, area, pH and habitat diversity. Pond area and isolation mesh with deterministic models of community assembly (i.e. models describing the patterns and causes of the combinations of species found in a pond). The image of ponds as islands is potent, pervading popular and conservation management texts (e.g. Kabisch and Hemmerling, 1984; Probert, 1989). Several myths of pond management (debunked by Biggs et al. 1994) are based on a deterministic view of pond ecology ("the bigger the pond the better") or avoidance of processes that interrupt predictable development ("drying out is disastrous for pond communities").

Published studies of pond-life show a less certain grip on pattern and process. Friday (1987) started her review stating that ponds are highly individual, the fauna and flora varying widely, unpredictably, between ponds within a small area. This sense of uncertainty has an older pedigree, explicit in earlier published studies of ponds. Kew, (1893), Godwin, (1923) and Fritsch, (1931), all emphasise "chance", reviewed by Talling in "The element of chance in pond populations" (1951). But mid-twentieth century ecology's greatest achievements included the development of deterministic models of community processes. The role of chance, in particular the development of communities contingent on past events, was largely ignored.

Coherent patterns and reliable rules partly depend on scale. At larger scales Britain's pond-life is predictable. There are recognisable northern and southern species and communities, the list of British pond taxa has been broadly the same for several thousand years. At an intimate scale there is predictability. Ponds usually have the same set of taxa between any two days. The unpredictability occurs at the medium scale, such as variations in the distribution of taxa between ponds in a region or over several years.

Recent studies of pond communities have shown reliable patterns e.g. culicid and dytiscid species richness increases with pond area, Nilsson and Svensson, (1995), and crustacean species richness increases with pond area, King et al. (1996), The unreliability of obvious factors such as area or water chemistry as predictors of species richness or association haunts many other studies (Barnes, 1983; Nilsson, 1984; Pip, 1986, 1987; Friday, 1987; Jeffries, 1989, 1991). Differences between ponds are increasingly emphasised as a natural, beneficial characteristic rather than a mystery in recent conservation advice (e.g. Countryside Council for Wales, 1996).

The contrast between deterministic and random models of pond communities is muddied by confusion of what constitutes chance processes. Friday's (1987) review was intended to show to variety of explanatory factors creating unpredictability between ponds. However each factor (e.g. area, pH, predation) is itself deterministic. The diversity of pond life arises from the diversity of causes rather than truly random or chaotic processes. Macan (1973) describing Godwin's (1923) study concluded that species richness increases with pond age due to plants' poor powers of dispersal and therefore that plant distributions do depend on chance. However dispersal that appears to create random patterns can still fit perfectly predictable models. A species of water beetle may disperse by flight, colonising 50% of ponds in a region every year (predictable) but which ponds out of the total may vary unpredictably.

None of this would matter except that the apparently unpredictable ecology of ponds has serious consequences for their conservation.
(1) The lack of reliable models may disillusion conservationists.
Myths of pond management, still widely credited coupled with our inability to confidently predict the future ecology of individual ponds undermines confidence and can be dispiriting. Questions from would be pond creators such as "how big a pond do I need to attract dragonflies?" or "What is the best sort of pond for this area?" meet with vague answers which may be interpreted as meaning the pond will have no value.

We need to learn to live with uncertainty, to relish unpredictability as an essential characteristic of ponds, a precious phenomenon.

(2) If ponds are naturally unpredictable and individual their landscape matters.

Deterministic rules, if they worked, might allow us to answer question such as how many species will be lost to a region if 10%, 50%, 80% of ponds are lost. But each pond may be unique. The connectivity between ponds may be complex as species disperse. Processes, chance or deterministic, vary at local, regional and national scales.

We need to understand ponds both for their individuality and also within a wider pondscape

This paper will describe the nature of chance and variation in pond-life, hopefully so that this essential feature of ponds is no longer seen as a problem but as a delight.

The nature of chance.
Chance patterns and processes.

Chance and unpredictability have been used to describe several different patterns and processes in ponds. There are at least four recognisable categories.

(1) Rare events.

Such events include colonisation by species or infrequent impacts such as severe droughts. Colonisations in this category include both rare species but also the establishment of species that, although widespread, seldom colonise new ponds. Colonisations or impacts may not be genuinely unpredictable but their frequency is so low (e.g. the return time of a particularly severe drought) that they are rare within the lifetime of a pond.

(2) Redistribution.

Many studies citing chance as a factor are referring to the vagaries of the redistribution of species, often on an annual scale. Dispersal and colonisation in such cases are common events, both in time and space (a species colonises sites every year, and many sites throughout a region) but colonisation of any one pond is unpredictable. This redistribution of species equates to species turnover.

(3) Contingency.

The development of a pond's community may depend on the presence of keystone species or the prioirty effect (which ever species establishes first maintains dominance subsqently). The impact (or lack, if absent) of keystone taxa on the rest of the community is profound. The wildlife of a pond may be clearly determined by the impact of keystone species. Such deterministic patterns are contingent on the previous history of the pond, especially the colonisation by keystone taxa.

(4) Chaotic dynamics.

Ecology made a significant contribution to the origins of the science of chaos, particularly through population dynamics and the idea of chaotic switching between alternative communities. Many pond taxa may show intrinsically chaotic population dynamics and vegetation changes in response to nutrient changes may be a form of switching. Submerged macrophytes often show changes in abundance between years which may be genuinely chaotic, lacking any explanatory trigger such as nutrients.

The influence of chance on pond biodiversity.

Biodiversity is an established focus for conservation in the UK and ponds an important refuge for rare species or component of habitats cited for particular effort (HMSO, 1994;

Biodiversity Challenge, 1994). Genetic, taxonomic and ecological components of pond biodiversity may all be affected by chance.

Genetic biodiversity.

Ecological geneticists have focused on genetic diversity between separate populations of microcrustacea. Microcrustacea are attractive subjects, given their passive, apparently chancy dispersal and the possibility of founder effects when a handful of individuals (perhaps only one, given that many are parthenogenetic), representing a limited sample of the full genetic variety within a species establish in a new pond. Boileau and Taylor (1994) review several studies showing genetic variation between populations of microcrustacea and show marked genetic divergence between populations of 4 out of 8 microcrustacea sampled from adjacent ponds, attributing this to chance colonisations by small numbers of founders (*contingent* development following on from *rare event* colonisation). Genetic diversity between populations of ostracods has also been credited to founder effects resulting from rare colonisation events (Little and Hebert, 1997). Recent evidence suggests similar genetic variation due to founder effects amongst populations of *Tubifex tubifex* worms from separate ponds (Anlauf and Neumann, 1997). The ultimate outcome may be speciation. Korinek and Hebert (1996) describe three new species of Daphnia from the USA, all restricted range endemics from temporary pools.

Pond ecologists generally do not work on genetics, but the limited evidence is that there are important variations driven by chance events.

Taxonomic diversity.

Historic interest in chance has concentrated on species' distributions, often linked to powers of dispersal, aestivation and interactions between species. There are, famously, individual ponds that might harbour the sole UK populations of a species (e.g. the Glutinous Snail, *Myxas glutinosa*, and Tadpole Shrimp, *Triops canciformis*, Biggs *et al.*, 1993). King *et al.* (1996) emphasise high levels of endemicity, rarity, even new species amongst temporary pool fauna, but the distribution of individual species was not linked to distance between ponds, suggesting an unpredictable scatter. The varied combinations of species required the sheer number and extent of ponds. Landscape and chance interact to create variations in taxonomic biodiversity. Chance distributions occur amongst the most common, mobile species. For example, amongst the taxa found in Friday's (1987) survey of 16 ponds many cosmopolitan, mobile taxa were not found in every pond (e.g. The Greater Waterboatman, *Notonecta glauca*, in 4 ponds, Large Red Damselfly, *Pyrrhosoma nymphula* in 13 and a dytiscid beetle, *Agabus bipustulatus*, in 8). Jeffries (1989) quantified this taxonomic element of chance for some 80 taxa found amongst 29 small ponds across a 400m long wetland. For each of the 80 taxa the ponds were divided into two sets based on the presence or absence of other species with which a taxon was associated; ponds in which each taxon was expected to be found or was not expected. Mean occurrence of taxa in ponds in which they were expected was 80%, or, if you prefer missing from 20% of pools. The mean occurrence in pools in which taxa were not expected was 11%. Even the most ubiquitous taxa were not found in every pond. Continued work on these ponds showed taxa considerable species turnover between years. New colonists species represented between 5-28% of the available species pool, numbers of species lost from ponds between 3-16% of the taxa in a pond. Colonisation and extinction rates for 10 common taxa were compared to predictions using metapopulation models. Results suggested for many species colonisation depended on the length of time ponds held water into the summer (redistribution chance events interacted with the variety of ponds in the landscape). Extinctions showed little correlation to ponds drying up. Instead biotic interactions may be important. For example predatory invertebrates may wipe out prey populations in the small ponds, (redistribution chance events as predators colonise leading to contingent alterations of prey populations as a result of keystone interactions).

So chance creates diversity in the distributions and combinations of individual taxa.

Ecological biodiversity.

Ecological biodiversity refers to recognisable, coherent associations of taxa. Use of the term "ecological community" implies an integrated, holistic suite of species assembled by predictable rules. Alternatively associations may be "assemblages", recurrent stets of taxa that happen to live in the same place for no other reason than shared habitat requirements and tolerances rather than any strong integration. An appeal to chance as an important ecological process seems to undermine the very concept of coherent patterns. This need not be so. Patterns and processes described as chance such as rare events or redistribution may can be predictable at some scales (e.g. the hypothetical beetle cited in the introduction that colonises 50% of ponds every year). Development of a community may be highly predictable once started but contingent on chance colonisation by keystone taxa. Ecological biodiversity includes other ecosystem characteristics than the associations of taxa, e.g. interaction patterns, food web structure and ecosystem functions.

Many recent pond surveys attempt to classify ponds into meaningful sets characterised by shared communities. Often this has the wider goal of producing standard classifications of pond types against which other sites can be assessed for their conservation value. The classification methods used, by their very nature, group ponds together based on shared species, inevitably denying the detailed variety of life; you do not want a classification system that ends up saying everything is different to everything else. Classifications of plant communities have yielded consistent patterns that are readily linked to environmental variable. Macroinvertebrate data produced ecological classifications but relationships with environmental factors are often unclear (Jeffries, 1991). The much greater number of invertebrate taxa, varied means of dispersal and different habitat requirements may result in much more diverse assemblages. Classification of ecological diversity across 34 Oxfordshire ponds (Pond Action, 1994) based on invertebrates produced much more coherent patterns, perhaps the result of much more intensive sampling over several seasons, so less vulnerable to short-term differences in species' distributions and abundance. The biodiversity of pond plant and animal communities differ in the importance of deterministic versus chance processes. Plant communities may be more predictable strongly correlated with obvious environmental influences such as pH.

More abstract aspects of biodiversity attract less attention amongst conservationists. Ponds have been used extensively for studies of food-web patterns and dynamics. There is good evidence that invertebrate pond communities (not just the taxa present but the pattern and number of links in the food-web) vary as a result of predatory keystone species whose own presence is partly the result of chance colonisation e.g. *Dytiscus* larvae impact on tadpole numbers Pearman, (1995), food web structure varying between ponds along duration gradient which affects colonisation, Schneider, (1997).

Chance and the landscape.

The significance of different ecological processes varies with scale. Many of the patterns shown by pond-life that are so suggestive of chance events are perfectly predictable. The interaction with the landscape makes them appear to be chance. The example of rare events and redistribution colonisations are good examples, influenced by numbers and relative positions of ponds. I have already cited the example of the species of beetle that colonises 50% of ponds in an area every year, but not necessarily the same ponds. Such processes may vary with the landscape. For example, instead of 50% of ponds regardless of how many ponds there are, colonisation rates may vary non-linearly, with colonisation rates of 100% above a particular density of ponds, below this threshold colonisation rates decreasing and a lower threshold below which no ponds are colonised.

Inevitably a paper concentrating on chance creates the impression I believe this is the sole or dominant influence on the ecology of ponds. I don't, but chance plays an important role which I suspect is intimately linked to the wider landscape though there is little, if any evidence, to unravel this complex, dynamic problem. Instead I hope this paper has provided some foundations on which to approach chance processes, to understand their nature and significance for the biodiversity of pond-life. Celebrate the unpredictability of ponds.

References.

Anlauf, A. & Neumann, D. (1997) The genetic variability of *Tubifex tubifex* (Muller) in 20 populations and its relationship to habitat type. *Archiv fur Hydrobiologie* **139**: 145-162.

Barnes, L.E. (1983) The colonisation of ball clay ponds by macro-invertebrates and macrophytes. *Freshwater Biology* **13**: 561-578.

Biggs, J.; Corfield, A.; Walker, D.; Whitfield, M. & Williams, P. (1993) The importance of ponds for wildlife. In Aistrop C. & Biggs J. (eds.) *Proceedings of the conference Protecting Britain's Ponds*. Wildfowl and Wetlands Trust and Pond Action, Slimbridge.

Biggs, J.; Corfield A.; Walker, D.; Whitfield, M & Williams, P. (1994) New approaches to the management of ponds. *British Wildlife* **5**: 273-287

Boileau, M.G. & Taylor, B.E. (1994) Chance events, habitat age and the genetic structure of pond populations. *Archiv fur Hydrobiologie* **132**: 191-202.

Biodiversity Challenge (1994) *Biodiversity Challenge*. Royal Society for the Protection of Birds, Sandy

Countryside Council for Wales (1996) *Ponds and Conservation*. CCW, Bangor.

Friday, L. E. (1987) The diversity of macroinvertebrate and macrophyte communities in ponds. *Freshwater Biology* **18**: 87-104.

Fritsch, F.E. (1931) Some aspects of the ecology of freshwater algae. *Journal of Ecology* **19**: 233-272.

Godwin, H. (1923) Dispersal of pond floras. *Journal of Ecology* **11**:160-164

HMSO. (1994) Biodiversity. *The UK Action Plan*. HMSO, London.

Jeffries, M.J. (1989) Measuring Talling's 'element of chance in pond populations'. *Freshwater Biology* **21**: 383-393.

Jeffries, M.J. (1991) The ecology and conservation value of forestry ponds in Scotland, United Kingdom. *Biological Conservation* **58**: 191-211.

Jeffries, M.J. (1994) Invertebrate communities and turnover in wetland ponds affected by drought. *Freshwater Biology* **32**: 603-612.

Kabisch, K & Hemmerling, J. (1984) *Ponds and Pools - Oases in the Landscape*. Croom Helm, London

Kew, H.W. (1893) *The dispersal of shells*. London.

King, J.L; Simovich, M.A. & Brusca R.C. (1996) Species richness, endemism and ecology of crustacean assemblages in southern Californian vernal pools. *Hydrobiologia* **328**: 85-116.

Korinek, V. & Hebert P.D.N. (1996) A new species complex of *Daphnia* (Crustacea, Cladocera) from the Pacific Northwest of the United States. *Canadian Journal of Zoology* **74**: 1379-1393.

Little, T.J. & Hebert P.D.N. (1997) Clonal diversity in high arctic ostracodes. *Journal of Evolutionary Biology* **10**: 233-252.

Macan, T.T. (1973) *Ponds and Lakes*. George Allen & Unwin. London.

Pearman, P.B. (1995) Effects of pond size and consequent predator density on two species of tadpoles. *Oecoloiga* **102**: 1-8.

Pond Action (1994) *The Oxfordshire pond survey. Volume 1*. Pond Action, Oxford Brookes University.

Nilsson, A.N. (1984). Species richness and succession of aquatic beetles in some kettle-hole ponds in northern Sweden. *Holarctic Ecology* **7**: 149-156.

Nilsson A. N. & Svensson B.W. (1995) Assemblages of dytiscid predators and culicid pry in relation to environmental factors in natural and clear-cut boreal swamp forest pool. *Hydrobiologia* **308**: 183-196.

Pip, E. (1986) A study of pond colonisation of freshwater molluscs. *Journal of Molluscan Studies* **52**: 214-224.

Pip, E. (1987) Distribution and species richness of aquatic macrophytes in a group of Manitoba ponds, Canada. *Naturaliste Canadien* **114**: 176-175.

Probert, C. (1989) *Pearls in the Landscape*. Farming Press Books, Ipswich.

Schneider, D.W. (1997) Predation and food wed structure along a habitat duration gradient. *Oecologia* **110**: 567-575.

Talling, J.F. (1951) The element of chance in pond populations. *The Naturalist* **Oct-Dec 1951**: 157-170.

Dewponds and Amphibian Communities on the South Downs

T. J.C. Beebee

School of Biology, University of Sussex, Falmer, Brighton BN1 9QG, UK

Abstract

The fate of dewponds and their amphibian communities on an area of the Sussex Downs was monitored between 1977 and 1996. Despite a proactive pond restoration programme there was an overall net loss of 21% of the initial number of pools between 1977 and 1996. Anurans (common frogs *Rana temporaria* and toads *Bufo bufo*) were nevertheless more widespread on the Downs in 1996 compared with 1977, probably because they colonised new ponds effectively. By contrast, urodeles (smooth newts *Triturus vulgaris*, palmate newts *T. helveticus* and especially crested newts *T. cristatus*) all declined over the same period. *T. cristatus* occurred in nine sites in 1977 but in just three by 1996. Total destruction of ponds was the most common cause of crested newt extinction, but at two sites the species disappeared following the establishment of fish populations. Various indices of amphibian diversity in dewponds are also compared.

Introduction

The chalk hills ('Downs') of southern England occupy a substantial proportion (more than 15% in the county of Sussex) of the total landscape and were among the first areas to be inhabited and modified by human invaders some 6000-7000 years ago. Natural freshwater bodies are rare on the chalk substrate, though a few do occur on impermeable clay overlays. However, livestock farming on the Downs was maintained for many centuries by the provision of dewponds, constructed by puddling artificial liners of clay and straw into excavated depressions and allowing them to fill naturally with rainwater (Martin, 1909; Pugsley, 1939). From the 17th century onwards these ponds became very abundant, averaging one per km^2 on the Sussex Downs early in the 20th century, until arable intensification starting in the 1940s rendered them increasingly redundant. Dewponds at their best support a rich variety of fauna and flora including all five of the widespread amphibian species, and can be particularly good habitats for crested newts (Beebee, 1977). Unfortunately these ponds have short life spans and are quickly lost when their artificial bases crack and go unrepaired. More than 70% of those present on the Downs between the rivers Ouse and Adur disappeared between 1950 and 1977 (Beebee, 1977). Since that time these hills have been declared an Environmentally Sensitive Area (ESA), a Sussex Downs Conservation Board has been established, and efforts have been made to ameliorate the effects of intensive arable farming. These have included a substantial dewpond creation and restoration programme, and in this paper I report on a resurvey of dewponds during 1995-96 covering the same area as in 1977.

Methods

Information concerning dewpond restoration and creation was provided by the Sussex Downs Conservation Board, the National Trust, and in some cases by personal observations. All ponds within the study area that contained water were surveyed for amphibians during the springs of 1995 or 1996, employing standard procedures for the various species (Beebee, 1977; Griffiths et al., 1996). Data were compared with those obtained in an earlier survey carried out mainly in 1977 (Beebee, 1977) but with a few further observations between 1977 and 1980 using methods similar to those employed in 1995-96 except that live-trapping and egg-searching were not done in the earlier survey. Numbers of species combinations were compared with the theoretical maximum of 31, i.e. $(2^n - 1)$ for $n = 5$ species.

Results

The fate of dewponds and amphibians

The changing numbers of dewponds and their amphibian populations within the survey area are summarised in Table 1. The survey also included two larger pools (>500 m^2 surface area), at least one of which was probably of natural origin. Of 33 ponds present in 1977, only 16 remained in 1996 and half of these were partly cracked and very shallow (less than 30 cm maximum depth in April). This was despite the fact that 11 of the original 33 ponds had been restored during the intervening period; two of these 11 ponds were already dry, and a further four were in a precarious condition.

Table 1. Changes in dewponds and amphibians 1977-96

	1977 Situation	Net losses 1977-1996	Net gains 1977-1996	1996 Situation
Ponds (total)	33	17	10	26
Good quality ponds (total)	8	3	10	15
Common frog populations	4	3	8	9
Common toad populations	2	1	5	4
Smooth newt populations	14	9	5	10
Palmate newt populations	6	3	0	3
Crested newt populations	9	6	0	3

However, 13 ponds that were dry in 1976 or did not exist even as remnants at that time have also been created, and thus conservation work has been carried out on a total of 24 ponds in this part of the South Downs. Restored and newly created ponds were with only one exception sited rough grassland subject to livestock grazing. Most were also fenced to limit or prohibit access by these animals. Unfortunately there has been a substantial attrition rate with these new ponds as well (three losses and three in poor condition) despite the fact that most were made as recently as the early 1990s, with the result that by 1996 there were still 21% fewer ponds than in 1977. On the other hand 15 ponds were judged to be in good condition in 1996 compared with only eight in 1977. Ponds were assessed to be in good condition if they were at least 0.5 m deep in April and supported extensive growths of macrophytes (covering >25% of the pond base).

Occurrence of all five widespread amphibian species in 1977 and 1996 is also summarised in Table 1. Several changes were notable over this period. First, anurans were found more than twice as often in 1996 as in 1976 and both species increased by about the same degree. By contrast, all three species of urodeles declined. This difference between anurans and urodeles clearly had two reasons. (1) Anurans survived better in the old (1977) sites than did urodeles, remaining at 50-75% of sites (*B. bufo* and *R. temporaria* respectively) compared with 33, 36 or 50% for the newts (*T. cristatus*, *T. vulgaris* and *T. helveticus* respectively). Although the frequencies of amphibians still present in original (1977) ponds in 1996 were not significantly different from those expected by chance based on the overall rate of pond loss, crested newt declines were twice as great as would be expected from pond destruction alone. (2) Colonisation of new ponds varied substantially between species. Of the five amphibians present on the Downs, *Rana temporaria* was evidently the most efficient coloniser. By contrast, *T. helveticus* and *T. cristatus* had no detectable colonisation ability over the study period.

Indices of amphibian diversity

Various measures of amphibian success in Downland dewponds are summarised in Table 2. Total records were 17% fewer in 1996 compared with 1977, though the average number of species per pond (combined used + unused) was essentially unchanged and the percentage of ponds used by at least one species of amphibian was substantially higher in 1996, presumably reflecting the increased proportion of ponds in good condition. However, the average diversity within individual ponds tended to lower values in 1996, with a small reduction in the number of species combinations recorded (nine instead of 10) and a rather larger reduction (17%) in the average number of species in ponds used by at least one species. This reflected a smaller proportion of used ponds with more than one species in 1996 (55%) compared with 1977 (65%).

Table 2. Biodiversity indices for amphibians in dewponds

	Year	
Index	1977	1996
Total records*	35	29
Percentage of ponds used	55	69
Average No. species per pond surveyed	1.06	1.11
Average No. species per used pond	1.94	1.61
No. species combinations (% of maximum possible)	10 (32)	9 (29)

Used ponds are those with at least one species of amphibian present. *, the sum of all species in all ponds, i.e. Σ Number of records in Table 1.

Discussion

The contribution of pond habitats to biodiversity is increasingly recognised in Britain and elsewhere, but there have been enormous losses of ponds in recent decades, mostly consequent upon the changing patterns of modern agriculture (Oldham & Swan, 1993; Biggs et al., 1994; Milton, 1994). The South Downs have been transformed by such changes but are now benefiting from a relatively high input of conservation management. They therefore provide an interesting example of how readily reversible the damage caused to the British countryside by modern farming methods will turn out to be. It is discomforting to note that even with a proactive conservation programme that has (on average) restored or created more than one pond per year since 1977 in the study area of some 150 km^2, there has still been a net loss of water bodies over that period. On a more positive note, the programme has essentially doubled the number of good quality freshwater habitats from eight to 15. It will be important now to maintain the momentum of this pond programme and achieve the double goal of both maintaining pond numbers and improving average pond quality.

The 1995-96 survey included more methods for detecting newts than were applied in 1977-80 and thus should if anything have overestimated population survival over the 20 years. Despite this, it was clear that amphibian diversity in Downland dewponds changed substantially during the intervening period. Older ponds generally supported large and often mixed newt populations but few anurans, whereas the newer ponds have been occupied quickly by anurans (especially frogs) but much less effectively by newts. Frog and toad spawn is often moved deliberately by humans and, in particular, that from garden ponds in which both species prosper (Beebee, 1979) is frequently discarded in countryside ponds. Ornamental fish also appear in dewponds from time to time, presumably from similar sources. Such anthropogenic transport rarely occurs with newts, and this may partly explain the greater colonising power of anurans. However, anurans are inherently more vagile than urodeles and are thus better able to cross inhospitable terrain between ponds. At least some of the observed colonisation pattern is therefore likely to be natural and reflect the different biology of the two groups. New dewponds are rapidly colonised by aquatic insects with the power of flight, especially odonates but also hemipterans such as *Notonecta* species and a range of coleoptera.

The question also arises as to why anurans were relatively uncommon in the older ponds if their colonising powers are indeed better than those of newts. This could be the result of a type of natural succession. Newts are highly efficient predators of anuran larvae (Cooke, 1974), and their establishment in large numbers, as often happens in dewponds, may eventually lead to decline or extinction of the anurans. All the long-standing anuran populations in dewponds were in ponds containing fish, selective predators of urodele larvae which may prevent the development of large newt populations (Beebee, 1979). On this basis, the lower number of amphibian species combinations and lower average numbers of species per pond in 1996 might simply reflect the different frequencies of early and late successional stages in the two surveys.

Smooth newts are the most widespread of the three British urodeles and their general success in dewponds was not unexpected. It was striking, however, that the other two newts showed negligible ability to colonise the new ponds. It was also notable that *T. cristatus* fared especially badly, not only failing to colonise new ponds but also disappearing from old sites more than could be accounted for by pond destruction. The two extra losses actually had a common and very specific explanation. In both cases fish, a mixture of sticklebacks *Gasterosteus aculeatus* and large cyprinids, were introduced to ponds very close to human habitation. Crested newts (at the larval stage) are highly vulnerable to fish predation and disappeared entirely within a few years of fish appearance. If the present rate of decline of *T. cristatus* continues it will be extinct in the study area within another decade. However, the current improving status of dewponds on the Downs offers the opportunity to assist with the conservation of this most endangered of the widespread British amphibians. There are several new or newly-restored dewponds of excellent quality, sited within suitable terrestrial habitat, in which *T. cristatus* should prosper if deliberately introduced. The large areas of inhospitable arable terrain between these ponds and the very few surviving crested newt sites, together with the distances involved (mostly >1 km), make natural colonisation unlikely. A proactive translocation programme for this species is therefore well worth considering.

Acknowledgements

I thank the Sussex Downs Conservation Board and the National Trust for information about dewpond restoration and recreation.

References

Beebee, T.J.C. (1977). Habitats of the British Amphibians, 1. Chalk uplands. *Biological. Conservation* **12**: 279-94.

Beebee, T.J.C. (1979). Habitats of the British Amphibians, 2. suburban parks and gardens. *Biological Conservation* **15**: 241-58.

Biggs, J., Corfield, A., Walker, D., Whitfield, M. & Williams, P. (1994). New approaches to the management of ponds. *British Wildlife* **5**: 273-87.

Cooke, A.S. (1974). Differential predation by newts on anuran tadpoles. *British Journal of Herpetology* **5**: 386-90.

Griffiths, R.A., Raper, S.J. & Brady, L.D. (1996) Evaluation of a standard method for surveying common frogs (*Rana temporaria*) and newts (*Triturus cristatus, T. helveticus* and *T. vulgaris*). *JNCC Report No. 259*, JNCC, Peterborough.

Martin, E.A. (1909). Some observations on dewponds. *Geographical Journal* **34**: 174-95.

Milton, N. (1994). Comment - Nature conservation and arable farming. *British Wildlife* **5**: 229-35.

Oldham, R.S. & Swan, M. (1993). Pond loss - the present position, in: *Proceedings of the Conference Protecting Britain's ponds*, ed. C. Aistrop & J. Biggs. Wildfowl & Wetlands Trust and Pond Action, Oxford.

Pugsley, A.J. (1939). *Dewponds in Fable and Fact.* Country Life, London.

Pond protection and enhancement in a development context

J.W.Campion

John Campion Associates,
Landscape Design & Environmental Management Consultants,
Oak House, 28, Grosvenor Road, Heaton Moor,
Stockport, Cheshire SK4 4EE, United Kingdom

Abstract

Ponds are under threat from changes in agricultural practice and development works of all kinds. Whilst agricultural change is governed more by market forces than by planning control, significant opportunities arise under existing planning legislation to achieve the protection and enhancement of ponds in a development context. Environmental assessment, the imposition of appropriate planning conditions and the use of planning obligations are important elements which may be utilised in this process. These approaches, together with the establishment of public-private sector 'partnership' arrangements and the drawing-up and rigorous enforcement of planning briefs for development sites are explored, with reference to case studies in north-west England.

Introduction

This is not an academic paper; it is based upon practice and observation and the evidence which I bring to bear in support of my arguments is largely empirical. Whilst ponds have in recent years attracted a great deal of interest and academic research, certain key developments in north-west England have taken account of the perceived ecological and landscape value of ponds since the early 1970's. This paper examines a number of cases where ponds have been retained, protected and enhanced in the context of significant urban development and seeks to establish pointers as to how ponds can be safeguarded in future.

Ownership

When the Warrington New Town Development Corporation was set up by the government in 1970, there were around 400 ponds within the Designated Area, and these came into public ownership. The brief for the development of the new town and its infrastructure could not accommodate the retention of all of these ponds, but the establishment of multi-disciplinary teams from the earliest planning stage provided an opportunity for serious consideration of their future. The teams included landscape architects and an ecologist, each of whom had theoretically equal influence over the planning of the three main development areas, Birchwood, Westbrook and Bridgewater, along with planners, surveyors, engineers, architects and social development officers.

Systematic ecological survey of the ponds and an evaluation of their potential for retention and enhancement within the planned open space system - the structural landscape - was an integral part of the landscape design and planning process. The survey results showed that many of these ponds were in an advanced state of succession to dry land, with deep water, steep sides, heavy siltation and shading being commonplace. Many had been subject to the typical abuse meted out by some landowners, who frequently regarded their ponds as convenient receptacles for waste, both physical and chemical. Where ponds could be rehabilitated and incorporated into the planned open space system, this was done, the work being carried out by contractors working under the direct supervision of landscape managers and ecologists employed by the Development Corporation. Where land was being sold for development, the use of detailed planning briefs incorporated as a condition of land sales ensured that all ponds and other significant landscape features were conserved both during and after development. A key element in this context was to make them safe, so that children in particular would not be at risk whilst playing in and around them, a sensitive political issue and one involving liabilities in law.

In all, some 200 ponds were retained, enhanced through remedial management works, and protected within an open space system transferred to the successor local authority, together with appropriate levels of management funding. Part of this transfer package was a Pond Management Plan (Commission for the New Towns, 1994), based upon a sample survey of 22 ponds in the Westbrook area. This document described the history of rehabilitation of ponds in Warrington New Town and set down future management guidelines and cycles of recommended operations.

Major factors in the successful retention of these features were that the ownership remained public and that the work was carried out in advance of development, so that new residents accepted these ponds as being a valuable part of their local landscape from the outset. This acceptance was greatly reinforced by the work of the Park Ranger Service, especially in relation to the study of natural history by local school groups.

Ownership and 'Partnership'

The ownership of ponds by a Development Corporation, centrally-funded and not subject to major political influence in its decision-making at the local level, might be seen as an obvious key to success. In the more common local authority context, it is perhaps more difficult to achieve.

It was therefore refreshing to be involved in a radical approach taken by a local authority to the matter of landscape and pond conservation in a residential development area at Upton Rocks in Widnes. In 1992, Halton Borough Council was seeking to develop a large area of land in its ownership in north Widnes, but was unable to provide the all the necessary funds itself for the construction of the physical site infrastructure and the conservation of hedgerows, trees and ponds on a former mixed arable and grassland tenanted farm holding. In 1991, the Council commissioned consultants to produce a development brief for this site, including the carrying out of a feasibility study into pond retention and conservation and the remedial treatment of the land drainage and ditch system, which had a history of local flooding. 14 ponds were subject to ecological and landscape survey, together with linking ditches. 12 ponds were retained and rehabilitated, and a new pond was re-created on a former pond site.

New ditches were created to link previously isolated ponds and existing ditches rehabilitated, with culverts placed beneath site access roads serving the new development.

This work cost around £98,000 and was secured as part of a legal agreement between Halton Borough Council and Redrow Homes/Beazer Homes. An agreement was made whereby part of the land sales receipts could be released in advance of development, with the private sector parties to the agreement acting as employer of the landscape contractor and the supervising consultant. With the private sector acting as employer, a contract was negotiated with a single, specialist contractor, which would not have been possible under the Council's standing orders, allowing for a rapid onset of site works during the most favourable season. The pond protection and enhancement work was secured by placing a charge on the sale of individual properties: the developer could not sell any one property unless he had fulfilled the legal obligations placed upon him. There was no resistance to this measure by the developers involved, indeed considerable good will continued throughout the site development process.

This use of powers under contract conditional upon land sales was seen as being more reliable and having greater weight than the enforcement of planning conditions or entering into planning obligations. Any default would have been remedied under contract law.

Influence

Where the ownership of ponds does not lie with a local authority or other public body, then the protection and enhancement of ponds in a development context must be dealt with by way of the statutory powers granted to local authorities under planning legislation, by agreement or by persuasion.

It is almost axiomatic to state that planners must know what they have of value before they can seek to protect and conserve it, and planners' lack of knowledge to date of the value of ponds as environmental features is probably a causative factor in the apparent decline in numbers and quality of lowland ponds. Current detailed research by Liverpool John Moores University and others should greatly assist the wider understanding of the value of lowland ponds in the United Kingdom, in both landscape and ecological terms. The government has recently adopted policy relating to the conservation of biodiversity in the United Kingdom in their report *This Common Inheritance* (DOE, 1997(a), referring to the *UK Steering Group Report* (HMSO, 1995), which included a Habitat Statement for Standing Open Water. The recent undertaking of district-wide nature conservation audits promoted by English Nature should allow planners to include in their Local Plan or Unitary Development Plan environmental policies the protection and enhancement of ponds. Once enshrined in adopted planning policies, protection measures can include planning conditions attached to development consents or grounds for refusal of a consent. In the latter case, defending the planning authority's decision at appeal is made easier by reference to adopted planning policies for the protection and enhancement of ponds. It should also assist the local planning authority in exercising their discretionary powers under the Town and Country Planning (Assessment of Environmental Effects) Regulations, 1988, as to whether to require an environmental assessment for a given proposed development (Schedule 2 Projects) which might affect ponds in the vicinity .

It is therefore possible for a local planning authority to place planning conditions upon the consent granted for any development to protect and enhance ponds within a given development site. For those ponds which may lie outwith the site but which might be adversely affected by the particular development under consideration, the use of planning obligations is now an established mechanism by which such measure might be achieved. Circular 1/97 from the Department of the Environment (DOE, 1997(b) is instructive in seeking to clarify the government's policy for the use of planning obligations. It is made clear that a planning obligation must only be sought where it is *necessary* to make a proposal acceptable in land-use planning terms. They should also be "relevant to planning, directly related to the proposed development, fairly and reasonably related in scale and kind to the proposed development and reasonable in all other respects" (DOE, 1997(2). This mechanism is flexible and based upon the principle of *agreement* between the local planning authority and the prospective developer. The use of planning obligations under Section 106 of the Town and Country Planning Act, 1990, has been a key measure in providing mitigation measure for the loss of ponds as a result of the construction of the Proposed Second Runway at Manchester Airport, allowing for works to be carried out beyond the limits of the footprint of the new runway itself.

Discussion

Ownership is clearly a major determining factor in considering the protection and enhancement of ponds in a development context. If the ponds in question lie within public ownership - such as that of a local authority or development corporation - then it should be possible to retain full control over all developments which are likely to affect the ponds. Warrington-Runcorn Development Corporation exemplified the effective working of this approach, and its interim successor authority, the Commission for the New Towns, continued with this approach in Warrington, Runcorn and in the Central Lancashire New Town area. Halton Borough Council again used their ownership of a major development site to protect and enhance ponds and other landscape features, whilst securing funding from the private sector to develop the necessary site infrastructure. Detailed planning briefs, able to be taken on board as conditions of land sale, are a vital component of the approach to site development. In both the Warrington-Runcorn context, and at Upton Rocks in Widnes, the importance of ponds and their associated drainage system was clearly stated, including provisions to secure the discharge of roof and land drainage water from landscape areas into the pond and ditch systems. These measures are intended to help to offset the loss of groundwater percolation through development within the pond catchment areas, in the interests of water conservation and habitat management.

Where ownership is in the hands of a prospective private sector developer, considerable reliance is placed upon the planning process and the fostering of a working relationship between the developer and the local planning authority n seeking to protect and enhance ponds. If the local planning authority has taken the subject of pond conservation and enhancement into its Local Plan or Unitary Development Plan environmental policies, then prospective developers should be aware from the outset that developments which might adversely affect ponds will be required to take account of the adopted policies. It is therefore reasonable to suggest that local planning authorities should seek to assemble all relevant information as to the conservation status of ponds within their areas as a matter of urgency, as a basis for environmental policy formulation. Nature Conservation Audits will be a valuable tool in this regard. In the absence of such information, as an interim measure it would be pragmatic to encourage the submission of an environmental statement by a prospective developer for any site which might affect ponds, allowing for relevant information to be gathered and analysed through the process of consultation with relevant bodies, such as English Nature, the Environment Agency or the local Wildlife Trust.

Conclusions

There is a widespread need for greater information as to the distribution and nature conservation status of ponds. Unless this information is gathered, evaluated and used as a sound basis for the formulation of environmental policies in Local Plans and Unitary Development Plans, local planning authorities will be significantly disadvantaged in trying to protect and enhance ponds under threat from development. Local planning authorities should seek to use their discretionary powers to require developers to submit environmental statements in support of planning applications for developments which might adversely affect ponds within the site and the surrounding area, in order that a proper evaluation of effects might be carried out. Public sector landowners should continue to take positive action to protect and enhance ponds within their ownership and include such works in their programmes for environmental education in the widest sense. Further research as to the nature conservation value of ponds should be promoted by statutory bodies and universities.

References

Commission for the New Towns (1994) Warrington Pond Management Plan (unpublished); issued to Warrington Borough Council as part of the information provided with the transfer of community-related assets.

DOE (1997(a) *This Common Inheritance* ; UK Annual Report, February 1997; pp.13 and 22.

HMSO (1995) *Biodiversity: The UK Steering Group Report, Volume 2: Action Plans;* London: HMSO, 1995; pp. 289-290.

DOE (1997(b) *Planning Obligations;* DOE Circular 1/97; 28th January, 1997

Manchester Airport Second Runway: mitigation in respect of the impact on amphibians and the re-creation of pond landscapes

I. Marshall[1], T. Walmsley[2] and A. Knape[3]

[1]Cheshire County Council, Environmental Planning Service, Commerce House, Hunter Street, Chester, Cheshire, CH1 2QP, UK
[2,3]Manchester Airport PLC, Hale Top House, Thorley Lane, Manchester, M90 5PR, UK

Abstract

Manchester Airport PLC has been granted planning permission to construct a second runway parallel to, but staggered from the existing one, extending across part of the Bollin Valley and on to the Cheshire Plain.

Over 230 ponds have been identified and intensively surveyed in a wider area around the development, divided into 7 pond clusters. Although the majority are shaded and silted, biodiversity is great: collectively the ponds support around 90 species of wetland plants, 282 aquatic and terrestrial invertebrate species (69 of which are uncommon), and 4 amphibian species.

The Second Runway impacts on the pond network by the loss of 46 ponds and associated terrestrial habitats: 24 of which have supported Great Crested Newts during the 1992-1995 period.

An extensive mitigation package has been designed to: (1) replace lost habitats (both pond and terrestrial); (2) rescue and transfer plants and animals, and (3); minimise any possible effects of habitat fragmentation resulting from the new runway. The aim is not only to ensure no net loss of ecological value, but also to reinvigorate the pond network which is gradually declining through natural succession.

The works will provide valuable lessons for the restoration of pond landscapes elsewhere in the UK and across mainland Europe.

Introduction

On 15 January 1997 the Secretaries of State for Transport and the Environment announced that planning permission was to be granted for the construction of a second runway and associated facilities at Manchester Airport. The decision followed an eight month public inquiry into the proposed development ending in March 1995, during which evidence was heard on the economic benefits that would accrue to the North West Region from the development, as well as the acknowledged local environmental consequences of increased flights and the construction of a 3,000 metre long runway across the Bollin Valley on 210 hectares of Green Belt land in Cheshire and Greater Manchester. As part of the proposed development, Manchester Airport PLC, Cheshire County Council and Manchester City Council entered into agreements under Section 106 of the Town and Country Planning Act 1990. The agreements are wide ranging covering topics such as

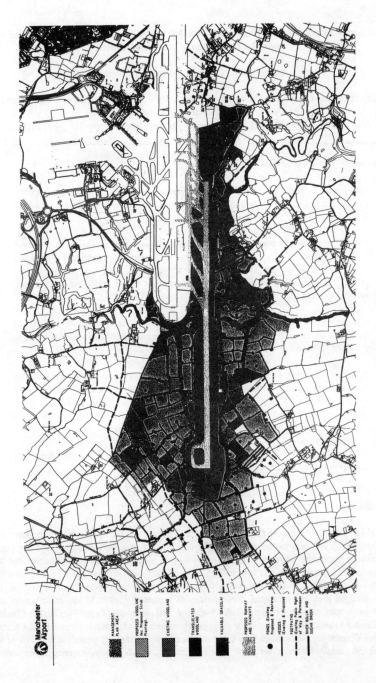

Figure 1: Manchester Airport Second Runway location

noise control, the establisment of a Community Trust Fund, restrictions on night flying and the promotion of public transport. In addition, the agreements require the Airport Company to provide an enhanced package of environmental mitigation measures over and above those submitted in the planning application for the Second Runway in order to reduce to acceptable levels the impact on landscape and ecology.

This paper summarises the approach adopted by the local authorities working in partnership with Manchester Airport PLC towards one aspect of those environmental works - ponds and amphibian mitigation. It outlines the principles involved and the planning, geographical and legal contexts within which these have been derived; and goes on to describe the methodology of mitigation.

The runway development in the local context

Manchester Airport lies in the northern part of the Cheshire Plain, a gently undulating area with an open pastoral landscape, punctuated with scattered farms and dwellings. The main exceptions to this pattern are the historic estates of Tatton and Styal, the Airport complex, the urban fringe (including a former brickworks site) and the Bollin Valley which bisects the site (Figure 1).

The nature conservation resource within the area reflects this landscape variation. A string of ancient woodland and grassland habitats and physiographic features are concentrated along the Bollin Valley. In contrast, the agricultural plateau above the valley is typified by widespread small copses, hedgerows and field ponds. Ponds and grasslands of more recent origin are associated with the brickworks and road embankments, located on the Airport perimeter.

The field ponds are representative of the pond-rich landscapes characteristic of the Cheshire Plain and parts of Lancashire, Greater Manchester and Clwyd. North West England has about 30,000 small water bodies. In Cheshire alone, there are an estimated 17,000 small water bodies in the size range up to 2 hectares (Boothby and Hull, 1997). Most owe their origins to the extraction of marl - a lime-rich deposit used over the centuries for spreading on the adjoining fields to correct the natural tendency to acidity and to maintain fertility. The marl pits filled with water and now constitute a significant wetland resource in these otherwise intensively farmed landscapes. Collectively across the region they contain all six native species of amphibians (including strong populations of the legally protected Great Crested Newt), several rare species of dragonfly, and many Red Data Book species of flora and fauna (Guest, 1997).

Cheshire may contain over 10% of all farmland ponds in England and Wales, and clearly has a national responsibility towards the conservation of this significant wetland resource. This is reflected in the County Replacement Structure Plan, policy ENV12, in which it is stated that development proposals which involve the loss of ponds will not normally be allowed, and that their conservation will be encouraged (Cheshire County Council, 1992).

The nature of the ponds

Over 230 ponds have been identified and intensively surveyed during the period 1992 - 1995 in a wide area around the development (Cobham Resource Consultants, 1993; Penny Anderson Associates, 1994a; Manchester Airport PLC, 1995). They have been divided into 7 pond clusters, separated by potential barriers, such as the A538 Wilmslow Road, the existing runway, the River Bollin or the lack of functional ponds. Of these, the Mobberley pond cluster is the most extensive, with 128 ponds and a further 28 on its fringes, and illustrates the considerable variety of pond types which exists. The majority are severely shaded and either permanent or largely ephemeral, but others are seasonally wet open, shallow hollows; open deep ponds; open or partially shaded pools with a floating raft of vegetation and; shallow pits which may never have flooded and support only damp-loving plants. This cluster supports a widespread, but relatively low population of Great Crested Newts, perhaps indicative of the poor availability and quality of terrestrial amphibian habitat of this intensively farmed land.

The group of ponds in and close to Oversley Ford Brickworks forms a separate cluster of particular significance for amphibians including a large population of Great Crested Newts. Rough grasslands and rubble provide abundant terrestrial amphibian habitat.

Table 1: Manchester Airport Second Runway - Summary of pond impacts and mitigation.

Impacts	Mitigation
Loss of 46 ponds (24 of which contain breeding Great Crested Newts, 19 breeding Smooth Newts, 22 breeding frogs, and 1 breeding toads)	46 new ponds created
	Improvements to 51 ponds
Loss of terrestrial amphibian habitat and hibernacula	Extensive habitat creation and improvement programme
	Provision of amphibian hibernacula
Fragmentation of Mobberley and Oversley Ford Brickworks clusters, and barrier effect of runway	Creation of interconnected network of habitats around runway
	Long-term maintenance and monitoring programme
Risk of death and injury to amphibians during construction	Installation of protective amphibian fencing during construction
	Capture and transfer of amphibians, as well as plants and invertebrates

Collectively, pond biodiversity in the vicinity of Manchester Airport is great: the 230 surveyed ponds support around 90 species of wetland plants, 282 aquatic and terrestrial invertebrate species (69 of which are uncommon), and 4 amphibian species.

The ecological impacts of the Second Runway

The impact of the construction of the Second Runway on the pond network is significant (Table 1).

Of the 230 ponds found in the survey area, 46 will be lost to the runway, of which 24 have supported Great Crested Newts at some time during the 1992 - 1995 period. Furthermore, 19 of these ponds support breeding Smooth Newts, 22 ponds breeding frogs and 1 pond breeding toads. In addition to the losses of aquatic habitat, the development would also lead to the loss of areas of terrestrial habitat and amphibian hibernacula. The Mobberley and Oversley Ford Brickworks pond clusters will be the most severely affected, and the Second Runway would sever territories and potentially create a barrier to the movement of species. The construction process itself could also potentially result in death and injury to amphibians arising from earth moving and vehicle movement.

The mitigation package

The detailed survey work commenced in 1992 for the production of the Environmental Statement and continued into 1996, and, combined with information presented during the Inquiry, provided the basis for the design of the mitigation package. Since the Public Inquiry, the Airport Company has produced draft designs and method statements for some of the environmental works, including ponds and amphibians. These contain more details as to possible methods of working, and have been planned to serve two purposes:

(i) to gain approval, in principal, from the parties to the Section 106 Agreement, as well as the local planning authority and English Nature, and;

(ii) to provide guidance to the contractor for the Second Runway as to a method of working.

The principles and objectives of pond and amphibian mitigation are fully explained in various Inquiry documents (Penny Anderson Associates 1994a, 1994b and 1994c), but in summary the package has been designed to address the following issues: (i) the number of ponds involved; (ii) their location when this is part of a cluster; (iii) the floristics of the ponds; (iv) the invertebrate diversity; (v) the needs of any amphibians present; (vi) proximity to good over-wintering habitat, and; (vii) the special requirements of Great Crested Newts because of their legal protection along with their habitat.

The mitigation proposals for ponds and amphibians include the following commitments:

- To adopt the principle of "no net loss" of nature conservation resource

- To provide at least twice as many new or restored ponds as those lost as a result of the development

- The provision of ponds to be guided by an agreed mitigation scheme, comprising:

  the creation of 46 ponds; the restoration of existing 51 ponds; the capture and transference of amphibians (as well as other animals and plants); the appropriate management of terrestrial habitat; construction of hibernacula; long-term monitoring;

- Detailed proposals to be submitted to and agreed with the local authorities in advance of the commencement of said works;

- Competent ecologists and landscape architects retained throughout;

- The establishment of a Nature Conservation and Landscape Steering Group to assess the impact and effectiveness of mitigation;

- Provision for long-term management of aquatic and terrestrial habitat and monitoring to be carried out in accordance with an agreed 15 year management plan over 350 hectares of land in the Airport Company's control.

This package has been agreed by all parties to the Section 106 Agreements, and separately by Macclesfield Borough Council and English Nature, who have helped refine the measures to meet their own concerns. Shortly after the Secretaries of State for Transport and Environment announced their decision on the development of the Second Runway, a joint venture consisting of AMEC and Tarmac was appointed as contractors not only to build but also produce the detailed design of the runway and the associated environmental mitigation works.

The strategy for achieving the commitments made at the Public Inquiry consists of realising five main objectives: restoration of existing ponds, creation of new ponds, translocation of amphibians, invertebrates, fish and plants, amphibian protection during construction and maintenance and long term monitoring.

The restoration work

The aim of the refurbishment work is to provide a range of pond types consistent with their marl pit character, in order to support species needing a range of different conditions.

The restoration works include one or more of the following: excavation of most or some silt to create structural diversity, removal and/or thinning of selected trees and shrubs (outside the bird breeding season), creation of adjacent marsh areas, enhancement of terrestrial habitat, construction of amphibian refugial hibernacula, establishment of a buffer zone around each pond, thinning of pond vegetation, and pond extension.

Strict guidelines have been developed to prevent the introduction of alien species into the newly restored ponds. In addition, plants rescued from ponds supporting fish will not be placed in amphibian receptor sites, nor be spread across more ponds from which they have been rescued. New aquatic plants will not be obtained from nurseries. This is to avoid the accidental introduction of invasive plants (such as *Crassula helmsii*) and fish eggs attached to the plants.

Marshes will be established from commercially available seed, but will be of native stock and preferably of regional provenance. Species to be used will be characteristic of Cheshire marl pits.

Plants used to stock restored ponds will be taken from ponds to be lost, or from other restored and existing ponds, in a way which avoids any damage to these sites. Plants will be taken, where appropriate, with root balls so that the associated invertebrates are also transferred. Plants will be introduced which are: suited to the environmental conditions (eg water depth, light levels) created, used by newts for egg laying (for ponds into which newts are to be translocated), already absent from the pond.

Amphibian hibernacula will be constructed around key receptor site ponds or as part of the new pond construction work. The hibernacula will be constructed so that their occupants are protected from frost at all times, are not flooded at any time and contain crevices where amphibians can find refuge.

Creation of new ponds

The function of the new ponds will be: to replace the ecological function of ponds to be lost to the development, for some to provide receptor sites for rescued amphibians, to maintain and extend the great crested newt cluster in a new configuration around the runway, to rejuvenate the pond clusters by providing new ponds to balance the considerable number of silted and shaded ponds. To achieve these objectives, the new ponds are designed to provide a diversity of types, in general copying the local marl pit dimensions, and including: shallow ponds which will dry out occasionally, ponds with some deeper water, particular requirements known to be favoured by the four amphibian species recorded in the area, variable slopes and irregular profiles in new ponds, marshy edges and flood areas, wildflower grassland on mounded subsoil from spoil, tall rank grassland, scrub/tree planting on the northern sector of a pond.

New ponds will be representative of the types of many pits found in the area. In each case, the bottom and edges of the ponds will be left rough to increase the surface area and assist the establishment process and where possible will be left to fill with water naturally. Some of the new ponds will be left to colonise naturally, whilst others will be inoculated with material (silt, plants and invertebrates) translocated from the ponds which are lost or from some of those being restored. The same principles will apply to the new ponds as to the restored ponds in respect of not introducing fish or alien plants.

The translocation process

In order to maintain great crested newt metapopulations, animals from clusters of donor sites (ponds within approximately 200m of each other) have been placed together in single receptor sites where appropriate. The larger Oversley Ford Brickworks population has been separable by pond in their new habitat. Refurbished ponds have been chosen for the majority of the receptor sites, principally because they will provide a better quality habitat more quickly than new ponds.

The translocation process has centred on the erection of temporary amphibian fencing (TAF) with bucket traps being used to capture amphibians as they return to or leave ponds, and whilst adult and juvenile animals are passing through suitable terrestrial habitat. Where it has been necessary that exclusion fencing enclose areas of terrestrial habitat around ponds pitfall traps have also been sunk within the fenced area.

Bottle traps have been employed extensively at the height of the newt courting phase to trap those which evaded capture on their way into ponds. Artificial egg laying strips have been provided, for example, strips of black plastic bags or similar cut into 5mm wide strips about 100mm long, tied onto canes. The strips have been removed to the allocated receptor sites on a weekly basis. Hand capture has been used to collect frog and toad spawn and any other amphibians seen in the ponds.

Drift TAF and pitfalls have also been erected across areas identified as good amphibian terrestrial habitat and likely amphibian conduits. The aim is to catch amphibians both approaching the ponds and those moving about their terrestrial habitats.

In those ponds which are rich in aquatic invertebrates and which support Notable or Local invertebrate species, a sample of the different invertebrates will be captured and moved to a receptor pond suited to their particular requirements. The animals will be captured by sweep netting in the vegetation and in the algal ooze covering the silt.

At the end of the capture programme the ponds will be dewatered and the TAF and buckets removed. An average sized pond will be emptied over a day so that any remaining amphibians can be captured and transferred to their allocated receptor site.

The contractors are employing, through their environmental subcontractors, 25 people who form the amphibian translocation team.

Amphibian protection during construction

Some of the ponds which do or will support amphibians lie close to the areas where construction work will take place. One-way TAF built at an angle of 45 degrees to horizontal has been erected along appropriate sections of the construction boundary to allow one way movement out of the construction area. In order to capture juveniles, which are less likely to migrate across the TAF, pitfall traps will be set in areas of good terrestrial habitat prior to construction work beginning.

Maintenance and monitoring

A comprehensive programme of maintenance and long term monitoring has been agreed with Cheshire County Council and Manchester City Council as parties to the Section 106 Agreement. Initially, an inspection programme of twice yearly visits during the growing season will be conducted to ensure that ponds are developing satisfactorily without pollution, physical damage, invasion of alien species or of fish into amphibian ponds, and exhibit good growth of introduced plants, establishment of animals and no algal blooms. Inspections will also identify any remedial or maintenance measures required, for example, for leaking ponds.

All ponds within the landscape and habitat management plan area, which will remain a working agricultural landscape, will be monitored following the translocation in order to: count frog spawn blobs, estimate toad strings, count numbers of adult toads by night searches, carry out netting and bottle trapping of newts, count newts in ponds which are safe to survey at night and count newt eggs. In addition to monitoring the amphibians the aquatic invertebrates and fish, and marsh/mud dwelling invertebrates will also be surveyed together with plant species present in the water and wetland species associated with the margins. The surveys will be conducted in years 1,2,4 and 10.

References

Boothby, J and Hull, A.P. (1997) A census of ponds in Cheshire, North West England. *Aquatic conservation: marine and freshwater ecosystems*, 7: 75-79.

Guest, J (1997) *Biodiversity in the ponds of lowland Northwest England.* Mimeo.

Cheshire County Council (1992) *Cheshire Replacement Structure Plan.* Cheshire County Council.

Cobham Resource Consultants (1993) *MA7: Manchester Airport Runway 2 Environmental Statement.*

Penny Anderson Associates (1994a) *MA761. Manchester airport Second Runway Planning Application. Proof of Evidence on Nature Conservation Matters. Tables and Appendices.*

Manchester Airport PLC (1995) *Manchester Airport Runway 2 1995 Pond surveys: Survey Report.* Unpublished.

Penny Anderson Associates (1994b) *MA760. Manchester Airport Second Runway Planning Application. Proof of Evidence on Nature Conservation Matters.*

Penny Anderson Associates (1994c) *MA769. Manchester Airport Second Runway Planning Application. Supplementary Evidence.*

Penny Anderson Associates (1994d) *MA764. Rebuttal Proof of Evidence on Issues Related to Natural Resources.*

Theme IV:

Strategies for protecting ponds and pond landscapes

The Pond *Life* Project: A model for conservation and sustainability

Andrew Hull

Pond *Life* Project, Liverpool John Moores University, Trueman Building,
15-21 Webster Street, Liverpool, L3 2ET
tel: 0151-231-4044 fax: 0151-258-1224
a.p.hull@livjm.ac.uk

Abstract

This paper considers the progressive loss of pond habitat in North Western Europe and reviews a major European Union initiative - the Pond *Life* Project - which, through community action, aims to present an effective model to protect and manage the valuable pond landscape of North West England.   Outputs from the Pond *Life* Project are examined and consideration is given to unique developments including the community pond warden scheme and regional pond networks, both of which have been established throughout the project area. Finally, consideration is given to how the positive achievements generated may be sustained after the Pond *Life* Project finishes in 1999.

Introduction

Field ponds were once a vital feature of most farming systems throughout North Western Europe but since 1945, as modern agriculture has intensified, the need for these small bodies of freshwater has progressively declined.   This loss, together with the removal of other significant features such as hedgerow and woodland, has led to an increasingly simplified agricultural landscape in which the protection of wildlife habitat and species has been overtaken by the unyielding demand to maximise production.

Although the loss of farmland ponds has been fairly well documented, strategies for their conservation and management still remain elusive.   A major initiative to redress this issue led to support from the *Life* Programme of the European Union (EU) to fund the multi-national Pond *Life* Project from 1995-1999.   The Project is based upon a partnership of public and voluntary sector bodies in the UK, Belgium, Denmark and the Netherlands and is utilising professional expertise, public resolve and local community effort.   Until the launch of the Pond *Life* Project mechanisms for pond protection, by and large, proved to be ineffective, sporadic and hardly ever sustainable.   The main thrust of the Pond *Life* Project is to place the task of pond conservation within local communities who can draw upon scientific, organisational and administrative expertise whenever and wherever it is required.

The Common Agricultural Policy, Ponds and the Farmed Landscape

The Common Agricultural Policy (CAP) of the European Union (EU) was designed to tackle production problems.   Although many of these problems were soon resolved, it became clear that the CAP was not only environmentally damaging but has also become a large financial burden. Furthermore, it is widely considered that the CAP conflicts with the habitat and species protection requirements of the Berne Convention, to which the EU is a signatory. Whilst sites of international importance have received habitat protection and management, their effect is limited to a relatively small number of locations. In contrast, many common but, nevertheless valuable habitats, such as ponds, have received little or no protection and therefore have attracted little consideration as a management issue.

Pond excavation over the centuries has created a valuable wetland mosaic over much of northern and central Europe. In the search for increased production, landscape features have often been modified and/or removed. This has been typical of ponds which are natural and semi-natural habitats of considerable ecological value. In recent years these habitats have come under increasing pressure from vegetational succession, urban encroachment, industrial development and a burgeoning transport infrastructure.

Table 1   The loss of ponds in Europe

Location	Dates	Pond Loss (%)	Source
UK			
Cheshire	1870-1986	60	Boothby et al, 1995
Essex	1870-1960	55	Heath & Whitehead, 1992
Sweden	1914-1970	55	Bjureke et al, 1976
Netherlands	1900-1989	90	Weinreich & Musters, 1993
Denmark	1868-1974	67	Briggs (unpublished)
Germany			
N.Rhine Westphalia	1963-1986	>40	Glindt, 1993
Berlin Sud	1880-1980	81	Sukopp, 1981
Poland			
Wielkopolska	1890-1941	56	Ryszkowski & Balazy, 1995

As Table 1 shows, throughout north western Europe there has been a progressive loss of ponds in the landscape. Several researchers have considered the implications of this on the populations of individual species and have reached the same conclusion of serious loss of biodiversity (see for example Sjogren 1991; Swan & Oldham 1994; Vos & Opdam 1993; Munsters 1995).

The *Life* Programme of the EU and the Pond *Life* Project

The *Life* Programme of the European Union was established in 1992 to contribute to the development and implementation of environmental policy by co-financing demonstration projects which support the fifth Environmental Action Programme. With an initial budget of over £500 million, the *Life* Programme aims to support a range of projects which promote the perspective of sustainable, lasting and environmentally aware development.

The Pond *Life* Project is a four year demonstration project, totalling £1.1 million, which will advance, interpret and apply the concept of sustainability to the development of small water bodies (ponds) to the planning and management of the agricultural landscape of North West England with applications elsewhere in the United Kingdom, and in a similar set of EU locations. Existing mechanisms for pond protection have proved ineffective, consequently the principal emphasis of the project is placed upon conservation by and within local communities. Local people will, in a supportive network, be able to draw upon scientific, organisational and administrative expertise provided by a working partnership of eighteen public and voluntary sector bodies in North West England, Belgium, Denmark and the Netherlands.

The philosophy of the Pond *Life* Project is built upon three principles:

- to think globally and act locally
- to take a holistic view of the pond environment
- to nest the project in a sustainable framework in the local community

Now in its third year of four, the project is building organically through agencies, organisations and individuals in a variety of sectors - agriculture and landowners, local community groups, local government, the voluntary conservation sector, academic research and enablers. For this burgeoning network a range of project outputs will help them in their work and these are shown below in Table 2.

Table 2   Outputs from the Pond *Life* Project

- Regional and county pond networks
- Pond Warden Scheme
- Critical Pond Biodiversity Survey (c. 1000 ponds)
- Geographic Information System - *The Pond Information Network (PIN)*
- Best Practice Manual
- Best Practice Video
- Workshops for key decision makers and volunteers
- Adopt-a-Pond Schools Programme
- Conferences and seminars
- Skills network
- Pond *Life* Consultants
- Regional Pond Strategy

Regional and County Pond Networks

As a response to requests for information about the Pond *Life* Project, a decision was taken early on to establish Regional/County Pond Networks. Two networks have been established in North West England, covering the Pond *Life* Project geographical area. Meetings are held twice annually with the overall aim of providing a forum for discussion and debate. Furthermore, they provide an opportunity for those not directly involved in the Pond *Life* Project being kept informed of developments at the cutting edge.

Table 3   Aims of the Regional/County Pond Networks

- to provide a regular forum for those parties who have an interest in ponds
- to raise awareness and information levels of key decision makers
- to increase protection of the pond resource and improvement of its habitat quality
- to ensure the emergence of a coherent regional strategy for pond conservation
- to ensure the recognition of strategic opportunities
- to facilitate no-net-loss of small water bodies and encourage net gain by creating new wetland features
- to exert influence upon Government agencies as to the need for the greater protection of the pondscape

---

It was widely accepted that in a region displaying such a dense pond landscape local authorities had been directly involved in pond related work for a number of years during which time many of them had developed firstly, considerable expertise and, more importantly, collected vital information about the pond resource. Additionally, it was strongly agreed that there should be a greater input from the agricultural community, particularly from farmers and landowners. As a result an invitation was sent to local branches of the Country Landowners Association (CLA), National Farmers Union (NFU), the Agricultural Development and Advisory Service (ADAS) and the Ministry of Agriculture, Fisheries and Food (MAFF). In all cases the opportunity for representation was welcomed. Finally, a range of other interest groups were invited - such as the Council for the Protection of Rural England (CPRE), the Countryside Commission, Groundwork Trust, Community Forests, Woodland Trust - all of whom have an impact upon ponds in both the rural and urban landscape.

The Pond Warden Scheme

At the core of the Pond *Life* Project is the Pond Warden Scheme. This scheme comprises community volunteers who are given the opportunity to become pro-active and look after ponds in their locality. Pond wardens will not only continue to monitor ponds within their patch but also, where possible, initiate remedial work on the more valuable sites as well as taking steps towards pond creation.

Community is useful shorthand for a variety of individuals and interest groups. It includes amateur naturalists and environmental activists; it includes schoolchildren; and it includes farmers and landowners.   But, pre-eminently it includes local people who are simply concerned with the preservation of their local landscape which is often seen to be an important part of their quality of life.

These voluntary wardens are not expected to be experts but they should display a genuine concern for their local environment.   Their principal task is to collect basic information about ponds in their locality and their exact location.   The collection of additional, more detailed information (biological records) is being encouraged and workshop sessions provide training for wardens who need, or are keen, to acquire skills in certain areas (such as plant and animal identification).   To help the Pond Warden in their task a Best Practice Manual is being produced.   This will contain useful practical information on pond management and creation together with notes about pond ecology, species checklists, pond survey sheets, useful contacts and other related materials.

Information collected by Pond Wardens will, with information obtained from a variety of other sources, be entered into the Pond Information Network (GIS) which is managed at Liverpool John Moores University.   The GIS will enable practitioners to investigate in detail the integration of pond systems and the relationship between the particular features of these small water bodies and a variety of other landscape criteria (for example, soils, land-use, farming systems).   Salient features of pond landscapes will be identified from the model and will provide the basic formula for a variety of practical initiatives to integrate them within modern agricultural systems and the environmental planning framework.   The ability to identify both 'critical ponds' and places where pond creation will strengthen 'corridors' or 'clusters' will be fed back to local communities where they will, once more take on the major responsibility of pond restoration and creation.

In all community-led schemes, such as this, there will be a need to retain the momentum and to tackle other issues which are of benefit to the local community, not only to those with a self-interest.   Motivation has to be maintained by offering practical guidance in the form of education and training, providing the grassroots actors with new skills There will be a need to regularly inform local groups of the reasons why they are carrying out such action, and there is a need to feed information back to the wider community so they too can see the positive benefits for themselves and for their community.   Finally, there is a need to set a series of identifiable targets rather than an eventual outcome which, in many cases, may well be some distance away.

Cooperation with the local farming community is a critical element in all aspects of the project operation.   The vast majority of ponds occur on private farmland and there is a need, for pond wardens in particular, to gain trust and respect from farmers who are, traditionally, suspicious of public involvement in their rural domain.

Pond Warden newsletters are now in circulation and are being prepared by the two Pond Community Officers employed by the Pond *Life* Project every three months..   Both publications - *Ponds for Life* and *Pondscapes* are distributed, firstly, to all pond wardens and then to a wider audience throughout North West England (see Jeffreys & Rooney, *this volume*).

In practice, the operation of a community conservation scheme such as this requires considerable input and in order to facilitate the scheme in North West England. It is the role of the Pond Community Officers to generate interest, raise awareness and encourage involvement. These tasks are not easy. Community awareness of, and involvement in such schemes, whether they be supported or not by outside agencies, is often geographically sporadic and what determines the genesis and subsequent success or failure of any scheme is related to a number of factors. Foremost amongst these factors is the existence of a core person, or small group of people with the time, energy, administrative skills and personal qualities to conceive a viable scheme and, by motivating others, to ensure its successful operation. Unfortunately, such people are not uniformly spread and their presence or absence is, again, dependent on a multitude of socio-economic factors. Furthermore, it has to be acknowledged that the work of local environmental pressure groups is not necessarily self-sustaining.

Towards sustainability

From the outset the Pond *Life* Project was designed to stimulate local activity capable of surviving the lifetime of the project. Indeed the nature of the EU *Life* Programme is to support and promote projects which are inherently *sustainable*. There is a need, therefore, to ensure that all elements of the project (*outputs, staff, premises etc.*) are adopted (*fostered*) by other agencies or organisations (*existing and/or newly created*) and will continue into the foreseeable future. A vital requirement for any short-term project, such as the Pond *Life* Project, is a clearly defined exit strategy. Projects which are conscious of their mortality and plan their departure effectively are more likely to leave behind durable bequests and achieve the elusive goal of sustainability ensuring a flow of continuos benefits. Two elements of the exit strategy are considered, briefly, below.

Regional Pond Strategy

Environmental conservation is now more central than ever in planning, development, countryside management, business and ethics. But there is still a need to expand the knowledge and understanding of many of its components. We must ensure that the means are available to identify what is special in the pond environment, to define its capacity for change; and, when deleterious activities or proposals for new development come forward, to assess their impact on the pond environment and give its full weight, alongside other considerations, in the planning process. Though the pond environment is largely a historical creation, it is necessary to plan for the present and future. Such diverse elements give localities their distinctive character and mark their individuality. They are also a significant contributor to biodiversity and to the visual landscape.

With these considerations in mind, we are attempting to define the elements of a strategy for the pond environment. This has to take into account the dense, rich environments of much of lowland England, but also of less-dense environments to be found in other areas both in the UK and elsewhere in Europe. Different national administrations have different histories, legal systems, planning frameworks, and political expectations. We wish also to begin identifying the key elements in this variation.

In summary, the purpose of the Strategy will be:

- to provide a groundwork of knowledge and understanding about the pond environment

- to put in place new initiatives for sustaining the pond environment and to develop policy responses to the issues currently confronting us.

At this initial stage in defining the scope of the Strategy and its content, it is proposed to involve statutory organisations, conservation bodies, and individual experts with a general interest in the pond environment. The Strategy will be positively shaped by comments at all stages in the drafting and at this stage comments would be welcomed from conference delegates of the scoping document in their information pack.

The National Pondlife Centre

This proposal, submitted to the Millennium Commission at the end of 1996 and currently undergoing detailed appraisal, is based upon the belief that there is a pressing requirement for the development of a permanent centre, dedicated to engendering the support and initiating the activity necessary to provide a secure future for Britain's ponds. The centre will carry out research, keep biological records, provide information and, through its dynamic outreach programme, increase awareness and promote further understanding of ponds and the benefit they can provide to the environment, the landscape, wildlife and people. The National Pondlife Centre is planned to be the first phase of a wider development which will see the creation of a number of smaller regional and specialist Pondlife centers at strategic locations throughout the United Kingdom. A more detailed account of this project can be found later in this volume.

Conclusion

There is every indication, midway through the Pond *Life* Project, that the issue of pond loss in North West England has started to be systematically and comprehensively addressed. Increasing contact with key decision makers together with a growing awareness of the principal issues of pond loss and their nature conservation value has started to permeate throughout and beyond the Project area. This has been achieved via a number of well defined and innovative pathways including the setting up of the community pond warden scheme; regional pond networks; conference, seminar and workshop; and outreach to farmers, landowners, schools and the wider community.

Despite these achievements a number of important milestones have still to be reached before the Project finishes in 1999. The publication of a Best Practice Manual and accompanying twenty minute video; a European Conference - *Protecting the European Pondscape* - to be held in Maastricht in September 1998; and a Technical Report outlining different approaches to pond conservation in the four countries involved in the Pond *Life* Project. Finally, the drafting of a *European Pond Strategy Policy Document* remains the final agenda item for a Project that has started to restore *Life* to the pond landscape of North Western Europe.

Acknowledgments

The Pond *Life* Project is a conservation project supported by the *Life* Programme of the European Union, led by Liverpool John Moores University, in a consortium of UK and European partners.

References

Bjureke, K., Dahlgren, U., Fronaeus, M., Hansen, C., Heister, V., Larssen, A. & Li, H. (1976) Margelgraver I Lundabygden; Environmental Protection Programme, Lund, Sweden.

Boothby, J. & Hull, A.P. (1997) A census of ponds in Cheshire, North West England, *Aquatic Conservation, Marine and Freshwater Ecosystems*, Vol. 7, 75-79.

Boothby, J., Hull, A.P. & Jeffreys, D.A. (1995) Sustaining a threatened landscape: Farmland ponds in Cheshire, *Journal of Environmental Planning and Management*, Vol. 38, No.4, 561-568.

Glindt, D. (1993) Situation, plege unt Neuanlage kleiner Stillgewasser im Flachland Norwestdeutschlands, Metelener Schriftenreihe fur Naturschutz 4, Metelen, Germany

Heath, D.J. & Whitehead, A. (1992) A survey of pond loss in Essex, South east England, *Aquatic Conservation, marine and Freshwater Ecosystems*, Vol.2, 267-273.

Hull, A.P. & Boothby, J. (1996) Networking, partnership and community conservation in North West England in Saunders, D.A., Craig, J.L. & Mattiske, E.M. (eds) *Nature Conservation 4: The Role of Networks*, Surrey Beatty Publishing, Chipping Norton, New South Wales, 341-355.

Munsters, K. (1995) *Poelenprojeckt Hasselt: Voorstellen voor het beheer en de aanleng van poelen in het gebied tussen Kermt en Stevoort*, Instituut voor Natuurbehoud, Rapport IN95.19, 13pp, Hasselt, Belgium.

Ryszkowski, L. & Balazy, S. (1995) *Agricultural Landscapes in Wielkopolska: Threats and Protection*, Research Center for Agricultural and Forest Environment, Polish Academy of Science, Poznan, Poland.

Sjogren, P. (1991) Extinction and isolation gradients in metapopulations: the case of the Pool Frog, *Biological Journal of the Linnean Society*, Vol.42, 135-147

Sukopp, H. (1981) Grundwasserabsenkungen - Ursachen unt Auswirkungen auf Natur unt Landschaft Berlins, in *Wasser - Berlin 1981: Vol.1, Die technischwissenschaftlichen Vortrager auf dem Kongress Wasser*, Berlin, 239-272

Swan, M.J.S. & Oldham, R.S. (1994) Amphibians and landscape composition, in Dover, J. (ed) *Fragmentation in Agricultural Landscapes*, Proceedings of the Third Annual IALE (UK) Conference, Myerscough College, Preston. 176-183

Vos, C.C. & Opdam, P. (1993) *Landscape Ecology of a Stressed Environment*, London, Chapman Hall.

Weinreich, J.A. & Musters, C.J.M. (1989) *The Situation of Nature in the Netherlands*, Den Haag, SDU Publishers, Netherlands.

The work of the Pond Conservation Group

C. M. Drake[1] and S. Pickering[2]

[1] English Nature, Northminster House, Peterborough PE1 1UA
[2] The Wildfowl and Wetland Trust, Slimbridge, Gloucester GL2 7BT

Abstract

The Pond Conservation Group was set up in 1991 to take forward ideas for conserving the wildlife of ponds. Its composition has remained informal and comprises representatives from statutory and other organisations. A strategic plan, launched in 1993, summarises the threats, value and interest in ponds, and lists six actions that will help to safeguard them. Model guidelines were produced for local authorities in their planning documents. The PCG initiated two bids for lottery funding for conservation action on ponds. The first project, to create 2000 new ponds, was unsuccessful but the second bid to restore 600 ponds, put to the Heritage Lottery Fund by a consortium of 23 organisations, has resulted in the Heritage Ponds project. Many areas highlighted in the strategy remain to be followed up. The group will continue to lobby for measures to conserve ponds, notably by persuading planners to take greater account of ponds in the landscape, and by continuing to present evidence to show how changes in agri-environment schemes can have positive benefits.

Formation of the Pond Conservation Group

The Pond Conservation Group (PCG) was set up in 1991 following a one-day symposium entitled 'Protecting Britain's Ponds', organised by Pond Action in September 1991 (Biggs & Aistrop, 1995). This symposium brought together ideas for pond conservation, and was probably the first on this theme with a nation-wide focus. While the threats and problems were well highlighted by this event, it was clear that no organisation was prepared to take the lead on implementing the solutions proposed by several speakers. Part of the reason for inaction was the lack a coordination among the many organisations undertaking conservation work on ponds. The suggestion to run an informal group was therefore welcomed and resulted in the first meeting in December the same year, with Pond Action providing both secretarial support and the chair.

About a dozen people attended the inaugural meeting and this level of attendance has been maintained since. Some of the organisations represented then are still active in the group six years later. Its composition has remained informal and comprises representatives from a wide range of statutory and other organisations (Appendix 1). Over the years, some 30 organisations or individuals either attend or receive the minutes of the PCG meetings, and therefore have the opportunity to contribute to its activities. Understandably, only a few organisations can spare time or personnel to attend the meetings but a wider representation would be welcomed. Because some organisations cannot or do not wish to become involved in lobbying Government, a distinction is made between those advisory members and core members. It was obvious from the outset that the group drew together a dynamic set of people with real expertise in science, policy, community involvement, media and lobbying, all led (sometimes driven) by an especially proficient chairman.

The remit of the group was initially seen as identifying and developing initiatives to promote the conservation of ponds, developing a pond conservation strategy, and encouraging the exchange of information amongst people involved in pond conservation. High on the early agenda were the need to investigate the feasibility of a statutory mechanisms for pond protection, and to promote better management. Not all the aspiration have been met but several important achievements are now discussed.

Pond conservation strategy

At the outset, producing a strategy was seen as the top priority, as this would direct further work and focus attention on the key issues. Before any strategy could be produced, the PCG recognised the need for a water-tight case to protect ponds, so its first year concentrated on this objective. A considerable amount of information was collated on a variety of topics, including the threats to ponds, its known wildlife interest, the role of local authorities in protection, and the scope of existing legislation in protecting ponds. This document became known as the Consultative Document and although, in the end, it was not published as its became too voluminous, it formed a valuable background for the early attempt to promote pond protection orders and for the first real product of the PCG, *A future for Britain's ponds: an agenda for action* (PCG, not dated).

The strategy summarised the key threats and values of ponds, which had not been done succinctly before, but central was a six-point agenda for action. This called upon Government to:

- encourage local authorities to make provision for the protection of ponds when preparing development plans, and to use existing planning legislation to prevent unnecessary damage to ponds;

- encourage the National Rivers Authority to make greater use of its powers in relation to ponds; to conserve and enhance the natural beauty and amenity, and flora and fauna of such water;

- extend the range of grants available for the management and restoration of ponds, and to encourage their uptake;

- promote the creation and maintenance of buffer zones around ponds through the provision of the appropriate financial incentives;

- introduce legislation to protect important ponds by means of Pond Protection Orders;

- monitor the number and quality of ponds in Britain through five-yearly surveys, and to publish this information on a regular basis.

It was realised that a high publicity profile was important if there was to be any gain from producing a pond conservation strategy. The strategy document was therefore launched in September 1993 at a press conference at Camley Street local nature reserve in the centre of London, where a pond, trains (for the press) and a meeting room come together. This nature reserve had the added irony that it was under threat from the proposed expansion of a railway station, thus highlighting the need for mechanisms to protect ponds. The launch was covered by several local and national papers, several magazines with specific interests (e.g. *Planning*) and national and local television. The PCG was pleased with the coverage which resulted in positive feedback from many quarters.

Copies of the strategy were sent to all county councils, conservation officers of the National Rivers Authority, statutory conservation agency offices, selected MPs and members of the House of Lords who were known to have an interest in countryside matters, and several other relevant organisations. The early responses to the strategy were encouraging insofar as the respondents were sympathetic to the case being made. The following year, copies were sent to all local district councils as it was felt that they were in a strong position to deliver some of the points that the strategy called for, notably the introduction of pond conservation orders and the provision of a better grant system for management. Perhaps most importantly, it was felt that local authorities could make a big impact through the planning system by identifying ponds in need of protection and incorporating better guidance in their planning guidelines.

The strategy was included by some organisations as part of pond information packs they prepared for their own activities, for example Eastleigh Borough Council's pond campaign in 1994 (Hampshire). In this way, the strategy reached more people than were sent copies by the PCG. A reprint was produced in 1995 so now there are about 3500 in circulation.

Planning guidelines

At the same time as strategy was being prepared, another important strand of activity was producing guidelines for local authorities to include in their structure plans, unitary development plans or local plans. The Town and Country Planning act 1990 (section 38) requires local planning authorities to include in their development plans policies in respect of the natural beauty and amenity of the land. Regulation 37 of the Conservation (Natural Habitats etc) Regulation 1994 provides for such policies to include those encouraging the management of landscape features of major importance to wildlife, such as ponds. Several authorities had already specifically mentioned ponds in their plans, and from these the best form of wording was culled, modified were necessary, and presented as a model (Appendix 2). These were sent to all local councils in England and Wales in summer of 1994, together with a copy of the strategy and a questionnaire about their development plans. The questionnaire revealed that about 30% of local authorities that replied had policies specifically designed to protect ponds, suggesting that there was considerable room for improvement.

Lottery funding

The latest major activity that the PCG has initiated is the successful Heritage Ponds Project (see Scott, this volume). This project is actually the second bid for lottery funds; its unsuccessful predecessor was the Ponds For People Project whose development WWF supported. The aim of this project was to provide grants to create 2000 new ponds within 5 years. This would involved a large number of people, so would have a strong community element, and provide ponds with the right properties for wildlife, rather than for fishing, wildfowl or amenity. However, the Millennium Commission rejected the proposal for a number of reasons. They considered it too ambitious and difficult to adequately manage dispersed voluntary effort. They required adequate measures for long-term maintenance of the ponds and were unable at that time to agree to funding umbrella projects which handed on grants. The PCG was understandably disappointed with this response because one of its aims has been to improve the accessibility of grants for pond creation. Funds for this activity have definitely declined in recent years, despite assurances from government that agri-environment schemes provide for them. Only by creating new ponds with wildlife as the objective will the future stock of valuable ponds be assured. A thrust on pond creation remains an ambition of the PCG. The shortcomings of the Ponds For People Project were rectified in its successful successor, the Heritage Ponds Project, although this aims at pond restoration rather than pond creation.

Pond conservation orders

Spurred by the representative from the Council for the Protection of Rural England (CPRE), the PCG discussed ways of promoting pond conservation orders as these seemed a likely means of protecting ponds that would not qualify as Sites of Special Scientific Interest (SSSI). Early in the PCG's deliberations, it was recognised that wildlife was but one aspect of ponds that needed to be considered if we were to gather a powerful body of support for their protection. Social history, archaeology, education and community importance were therefore all included in the case being made for protecting ponds. Criteria for a conservation order covered these areas and also geological and amenity value, and occurrence in degraded areas where any pond was likely to be of some value.

In the end it was decided to drop this line of approach for several reasons. The government of the day was obviously so against regulation that the chance of successful legal change was very low; in December 1994 the Environment Minister said: "The most valuable ponds will continue to receive protection through the SSSI system and environmental land management schemes will continue to include provisions for pond creation and protection. In the meantime, the Government sees no merit in introducing any further statutory protection for ponds". The slow development of the Hedgerow Incentive Scheme suggests that gestation for pond conservation legislation could be measured in decades, not years. The experience of Pond *Life* Project has concluded that pond conservation orders would alienate the huge body of support that it had uncovered through the parish pond warden scheme. Greater use of *Planning Policy Guidance No. 9: Nature Conservation* (DoE, 1994) is probably a more politically acceptable approach, although at the cost of occasional destruction of prime ponds by unsympathetic landowners. With the change in government and the current review of wildlife legislation, there may be opportunities that the PCG should be ready to take soon, especially now that scientifically sound methods of evaluating pond quality are being developed.

Other achievements and failures

Although the PCG can point to these main achievements, there are a number of spin-offs that have resulted from the group's existence. Increased networking between organisations with an interest in ponds is probably the most important outcome, and in turn has stimulated actions and products that may not otherwise have been pursued. These include proposed issue of stamps featuring ponds, being promoted by the British Wildfowl Association, the booklet *Managing ponds for wildlife* (English Nature & Pond Action, 1996), the inclusion of ponds in English Nature's recently published Freshwater Strategy (English Nature, 1997) and the collaboration between Pond Action and the Pond *Life* Project leading to this conference. The group is even mentioned in the Government's report on biodiversity (Hmso, 1994).

In other ways the PCG has not met its early ambitions of being the focus for organisations interested pond conservation. Part of this failure is due to attempting to run on a shoe-string. The group has no formal composition and no source of funding. The considerable secretarial costs have been born mainly by Pond Action, with support from some of the more active participating organisations and some sponsors to whom the PCG is most grateful. Another reason for a number of early ambitions not reaching fruition is the loss of the key promoter; it is clear that some actions were driven by a single individual whose input and enthusiasm had been crucial. An example is an early drive to produce a strategy for buffer zones that CPRE were particularly keen on.

A paradoxically good reasons for some activities becoming sidelined is that other groups or organisations have taken on the roles and activities themselves. The PCG is delighted to think that their work may have contributed to fostering an atmosphere in which these actions have become acceptable. Most importantly among these are the increasing number of booklets that provide good management advice (e.g. BTCV, 1996), the complementary work undertaken through the Pond *Life* Project, the uptake by the Department of the Environment of pond monitoring through the Countryside 2000 surveys, the specific inclusion of ponds in PPG9 as an example of a habitat whose management needs encouraging, and the much more positive attitude of the Environment Agency to ponds, as reflected in their management guidelines (Samson & Walmsley, 1993).

The future of the PCG

The PCG frequently examines the need for its own existence, and each time decides that there are actions in its strategy that still deserve attention. Lobbying and promoting awareness of the need for conservation action remain the most important immediate and medium-term roles for the group in the absence of secure funding for more ambitious aims. The group will follow up the effectiveness of local authority development plans for policies to protect ponds, press for mechanisms to include effective buffer zones at each review of the agri-environment schemes, and continue the pressure to re-instate grants for pond creation primarily for wildlife. The Biodiversity Action Plan presents a new opportunity for the PCG to influence habitat plans at a national and local scale. Creating ponds on a large scale may require the group to turn again to lottery or other source of funding.

The PCG holds meetings two or three times a year and is currently under the chairmanship of The Wildfowl and Wetland Trust. Minutes are circulated to organisations who may not be able to attend the meetings but who wish to be kept informed. If you would like to hear more about the group's activities, please contact Simon Pickering (WWT) on 01453 890333, or Martin Drake (English Nature) on 01733 455264.

Acknowledgements

The PCG owes a huge indebtedness to the no-nonsense chairmanship of Anne Powell, the secretarial support of Pond Action, grants from English Nature for the strategy document, and the enthusiasms of many of the group's members who would probably rather not be singled out.

References

Biggs, J. & Aistrop, C. (1995) *Protecting Britain's ponds.* Pond Conservation Group, Oxford.

BTCV (1996) *Pond campaign.* British Trust for Conservation Volunteers, Wallingford.

CPRE & Pond Action (1994) *Ponds.* Council for the Protection of Rural England, London.

DoE (1994) *Planning policy guidelines: nature conservation. No 9.* HMSO, London.

Drake, C. M., Williams, P., Biggs, J., & Whitfield, M. (1996) *Managing ponds for wildlife.* English Nature, Pond Action & National Rivers Authority.

English Nature (1997) *Wildlife and fresh water; an agenda for sustainable management.* English Nature, Peterborough.

Hmso (1994) *Biodiversity: the UK action plan.* HMSO, London.

Hmso (1995) *Biodiversity: the UK steering group report.* HMSO, London.

Pond Conservation Group (1992). *Legislation affecting ponds in Britain.* Unpublished report.

Pond Conservation Group (1993). *Protecting Britain's ponds - sources of information to support the campaign for a pond protection order.* Unpublished report.

Pond Conservation Group (not dated; 1993). *A future for Britain's ponds: an agenda for action.* Pond Conservation Group.

Sansom, A. & Walmsley, R. (1993) *Ponds and conservation. A rough guide to pond restoration, creation and management.* National Rivers Authority, Northumbria and Yorkshire Region.

Appendix 1. Organisations with past or present representatives on the Pond Conservation Group.

British Dragonfly Society
British Herpetological Society
British Waterfowl Association
Council for the Protection of Rural England
English Nature
Environment Agency
Ian Benton Ponds
Liverpool John Moores University

Northamptonshire County Council
Pond Action
Surrey Wildlife Trust
The Natural History Museum
The Wildlife Trusts Partnership
Wildfowl & Wetland Trust
World Wide Fund for Nature

Appendix 2. Protection of ponds: guidance for local planning authorities

Introduction

Ponds are small bodies of water up to 2 ha in size, which hold water for at least four months of the year. They are important wildlife habitats supporting a wide variety of wetland plants and animals, many of which are becoming rare or endangered. In many areas of the country, ponds are equally important as elements of the landscape and as part of the historical and cultural heritage of the region. They are also a valuable education resource for teaching a variety of subjects including biology, geography, community relations, mathematics, English, art, drama and many others.

Surveys in England and Wales indicate that 65% of ponds (approximately 500,000) have been lost in the last 100 years. In Britain as a whole, ponds are still being lost at a rate of 1% (4,000 ponds) per year. Changes in agriculture, increased land drainage, neglect, infilling and development have all contributed to this loss of ponds.

The role of Local Planning Authorities

Although currently there is no specific legislative protection for ponds, protection of varying degrees can be provided by the land use and planning system. A number of measures and policies that, if adopted by local planning authorities, would ensure greater protection for ponds are outlined below.

Regional Planning Guidance

When drawing up Regional Planning Advice, local planning authorities should identify protection of landscape features, wildlife and local character as an important strategic objective. In regions where ponds are an important component of the landscape, or under particular threat, they will warrant a specific mention in Regional Planning Advice. This will contribute to better Regional Planning Guidance from the Department of the Environment.

County Structure Plans

A strategic objective of Structure Plans should be the protection and enhancement of local character and distinctiveness in the landscape and the protection of wildlife resource. This cannot be achieved solely through landscape designation but must take into account the landscape and wildlife throughout the whole plan area.

Strategic policies designed to protect ponds

1. Developments will not normally be allowed that may destroy or adversely affect a designated or proposed Site of Special Scientific Interest, a National Reserve, a Local Nature Reserve, a National Park, an AONB and other area of landscape or historic importance identified by the local planning authority.

2. Outside designated areas, development will not be permitted if it is likely to cause a loss of habitat or features which are important for landscape, nature conservation or historic resource, unless it can be demonstrated to the satisfaction of the local planning authority that the need for the development overrides the environmental interest and no appropriate alternative site is available.

Local Plans and Unitary Development Plans (part II)

The Planning and Compensation Act 1991 places a new requirement on local planning authorities to include policies on the 'conservation of natural beauty and amenity of land' in development plans. In many regions, ponds make an important contribution to the natural beauty and amenity of land and, therefore, their protection should be an important element of Local Plans.

Policies to protect important landscape features and habitats including ponds

3. The council will not normally permit development which would lead to the loss or significant alteration of important habitats such as heathland, woodland, water meadows, unimproved pasture, marshes, streams, ponds or parks, especially those which support legally[1] protected or rare species or a rich assemblage of invertebrates or plants.

4. The council, where appropriate, will require planning applications to be supported by a full site survey and demonstrate that account has been taken of existing landscape features and wildlife.

5. The council will normally require proposals for the development, or redevelopment, to be accompanied by landscaping schemes of high standard which provide for the retention and enhancement of those existing features of nature conservation or landscape value and the protection of such features from damage during construction work or other development.

6. The council recognises the community and educational benefits associated with nature conservation and will, therefore, seek to realise opportunities for habitat retention, restoration, creation, and sympathetic management in public open spaces or on any land held or managed by the local authority.

7. The council will promote the conservation and enhancement of natural beauty and amenity

of the countryside including its flora and fauna, geological and physiographical features, and of any feature of archaeological or historical interest.

Policies specifically to protect and enhance ponds

8. The council will not normally grant planning permission for development which would adversely affect the landscape, historical or wildlife value of any existing pond or watercourse.

9. The council will promote the conservation of ponds and wetlands, especially where they contain scheduled species, rare species, or support a rich assemblage of invertebrate or plant species.

10. The council will protect archaeological features from any work which results in the demolition, or destruction of, or any damage to historic sites, to include dew and decoy ponds, fishponds, moats, leats and locks which are of historic value.

11. In areas where there has been a significant loss of ponds, the council will encourage the re-creation of ponds and as far as it is within its power, require that new ponds and wetland areas are designed to be sympathetic to the landscape and to provide rich and varied wildlife habitats.

Surveys

Planning Policy Guidance Note 12 (Development Plans and Regional Guidance, Feb 1992) provides advice to local planning authorities on the need to undertake surveys of their area prior to the preparation of Local Plans. These should include an audit of pond resources in the area and an assessment of their landscape, wildlife, historic and other value. Many local planning authorities already undertake assessment of landscape character which should include a reference to ponds. Such assessments are encouraged in Planning Policy Guidance Note 7 (The Countryside and the Rural Economy, Jan 1992).

Monitoring

Planning Policy Guidance Note 12 advises local planning authorities to monitor and review the effectiveness of local plans. The protection afforded to valued landscape features, such as ponds, should be an important component of any monitoring exercise.

Development Control

Local planning authorities should ensure that any environmental assessments required under the 1988 Regulations adequately address the impact of any proposed development on ponds and other landscape features where this is an important consideration.

Local planning authorities should require prospective developers to submit sufficient details with their planning applications to allow the potential impact on ponds to be examined. Where this is not forthcoming, local planning authorities should use their powers under the General

Development Order to require it to be provided.

In considering planning applications, councils should, as general policy, not normally consider the creation of habitat or landscapes features such as ponds or wet meadows to be adequate compensation or justification for any destruction of comparable features caused by the same development.

[1] Pond wildlife protected under the Wildlife and Countryside Act 1981.

Ponds support not only a wide variety of common wetland wildlife, but a number of rare and endangered plant and animals which are afforded protection under the Wildlife and Countryside Act 1981. Of the most vulnerable plant species - those listed in Schedule 8 of the Act - the following are dependant on ponds: Water Plantain *Alisma gramineum*, Creeping Marshwort *Apium repens*, Pigmyweed *Crassula aquatica*, Brown Galingale *Cyperus fuscus,* Starfruit *Damasonium alisma*, Welsh mudwort *Limosella autralis*, Grass-poly *Lythrum hyssopifolia*, Pennyroyal *Mentha puliginum*, Small Fleabane *Pulicaria vulgaris*, and Adder's-tongue spearwort *Ranunculus ophioglossifolius*.

Freshwater invertebrates dependant on ponds are given full protection by Schedule 5. These are: Glutinous snail *Myxas glutinosa*, Tadpole shrimp *Triops cancriformis*, Fairy shrimp *Chirocephalus diaphanus*, Medicinal leech *Hirudo medicinalis*, the Spangled water beetle *Graphoderus zonatus*, the Lesser Silver water beetle *Hydrochara caraboides*, the water beetle *Paracymus aeneus*, and the Fen Raft spider *Dolomedes plantarius*.

Two of the 6 species of native amphibians are given full protection under Schedule 5, the Natterjack Toad *Bufo calamita* and the Great Crested Newt *Triturus cristatus*.

Legislative and tenancy mechanisms for pond protection and management

J.M. Mackay

Joint Countryside Advisory Service, Bryant House, Liverpool Road North,
Maghull, Merseyside L31 2PA, UK

Abstract

The degree of protection afforded to ponds in the agricultural landscape by relevant legislation is assessed. Applicable enabling legislation includes the Town and Country Planning and Planning and Compensation Acts, Environment and Environmental Protection Acts, Water Resources Act, Wildlife and Countryside Act and Agricultural Tenancies Act, along with many associated regulations for waste management licensing, permitted development, tree preservation orders and hedgerow protection. Mechanisms for protection and management within this framework, including the use of planning obligations, planning and licence conditions and tenancy agreements, are given. Existing mechanisms are complex, difficult to administer and give incomplete protection. A need for specific planning protection of ponds to complement work on creation and management of ponds is identified.

Introduction

Protection is afforded to ponds, both directly through legislation (including planning, pollution control and waste management legislation) and indirectly through protection of features associated with ponds such as trees, protected species and hedgerows. However, existing protection or management powers are infrequently implemented, probably because of uncertainty of the applicability of these powers. This review assesses the mechanisms available through existing legislation, other means of protection and management, actions that could be carried out to assist in pond protection and the need for specific pond protection measures.

Legislative protection

Town and Country Planning

The origins of Town and Country Planning legislation in Britain lie largely in the prevention of urban development of the countryside. Currently embodied in the Town and Country Planning Act 1990 and Planning and Compensation Act 1991, planning legislation is slowly beginning to exert control over agricultural development. With some exceptions, agricultural development remains permitted development, with local planning authorities (LPAs) given the power to control factors such as siting and appearance but not to determine the principle of development.

Permitted development on different sizes of agricultural units is defined by Part 6 of the General Permitted Development Order 1995 (the GPDO). Class A includes "The carrying out on agricultural land comprised in an agricultural unit of 5 hectares or more in area of ... any ... engineering operations, which are reasonably necessary for the purposes of agriculture within that unit". Class B includes "The carrying out on agricultural land comprised in an agricultural unit of not less than 0.4 but less than 5 hectares in area of development consisting of ... the deposit of waste ... where the development is reasonably necessary for the purposes of agriculture."

It may seem from these definitions that a farmer does not require planning permission or need to notify the LPA in order to carry out the engineering operation of infilling a pond, as the farmer can claim that removal of a pond facilitates easier cultivation of a field and hence is necessary for agriculture. However, Class A permitted development is subject to the condition that "waste materials shall not be brought on to the land from elsewhere for deposit except for use in works [for the erection, extension or alteration of a building] or in the provision of a hard surface". This condition was introduced due to concerns over operations on farms in the past that were ostensibly for agriculture but were in reality for waste disposal. A similar condition limits the deposition of waste on the smaller farm units of Class B.

It is thus clear that planning permission is required if waste to infill a farm pond has to be imported. Obviously this does not cover the occasions when a farmer tips waste generated on the farm into a farm pond, but nevertheless a degree of protection does exist.

A particular difficulty experienced by LPAs in this context arises in defining "waste materials". Other legislation and European Directives define waste or classifications of waste, but the GPDO itself does not. Case law is conflicting, and it is not always obvious that material can definitely be considered imported waste. Inevitably, when it is observed that a pond is being infilled with imported waste without planning permission, there is a reluctance to proceed with enforcement action if there is uncertainty. A simple change in the GPDO, or a cross-reference to other legislation, clarifying how "waste materials" is to be construed in this specific context would be desirable.

If planning permission is required, it is not inevitable that permission will be refused. Many considerations should be taken into account when arriving at a balanced judgement, although historically the need for agricultural improvement has been a dominant consideration. For example, when planning permission was granted by Merseyside County Council in 1982 for the infilling of a pond in Tarbock with waste (concrete hardcore), no consideration appears to have been given to ecological interests. A lesson learned from this particular case is the danger of allowing such an activity to be initiated: from observation of aerial photography of the period, the operation was extended to destroy at least 13 ponds on the farm concerned in that one year.

Waste Management Licensing

In the United Kingdom, planning and waste management are controlled by different legislative frameworks. Waste management is largely controlled by the Environmental

Protection Act 1990 and the Waste Management Licensing Regulations 1994. Section 33 of the 1990 Act makes it an offence to deposit controlled waste in or on any land without a waste management licence or to treat, keep or dispose of controlled waste in or on any land except in accordance with a waste management licence.

Regardless of the need for planning permission, the Environment Agency, which grants such licences and is charged with protection of the environment, could, by refusing to grant a licence to infill a pond, protect ponds. However, several exemptions from waste management licensing could be applicable. For instance, spreading of some types of waste on agricultural land does not require a licence if it results in benefit to agriculture. Moreover, different sections of the Environment Agency deal with waste licensing and pollution control, and this introduces an administrative complexity.

Controlled Waters

A proposal to infill a pond is initially considered by the Environment Agency in the context of impact on controlled waters under the Water Resources Act 1991 and the Environment Act 1995. The Agency has the power under this legislation to carry out works to prevent any poisonous, noxious or polluting matter or any solid waste matter from entering controlled waters and to recover costs from anyone who caused or knowingly permitted this to occur. Usefully, this includes the power to require the restoration, so far is is reasonably practicable to do so, of restoring the waters, including the flora and fauna dependent on the aquatic environment of the waters.

For those ponds which may be considered controlled waters (this depends upon their having an inlet and outlet or, perhaps, on their hydrological connection to groundwater), the powers specified above are potentially a very powerful tool in retention.

The complex and inter-related waste licensing, pollution control and planning issues raised by infilling ponds with waste have yet to be addressed in detail. It would be useful for LPAs and the Environment Agency to address this jointly, particularly as the introduction of a landfill tax in 1996 has led to increased unauthorised or exempt waste deposits on farmland in the United Kingdom.

Protected Species

Part 1 of the Wildlife and Countryside Act 1981 sets out the protection which is afforded to wild animals and plants. The Schedules to the Act relating to protected animals (Schedule 5) and plants (Schedule 8) are reviewed every five years. Subject to certain provisions, a person who damages or destroys any place which any wild animal included in Schedule 5 uses for shelter or protection, or disturbs any such animal while it is occupying a structure or place which it uses for that purpose, shall be guilty of an offence. Subject to certain provisions, a person who intentionally picks, uproots or destroys any wild plant included in Schedule 8, or, not being an authorised person, intentionally uproots any wild plant not included in that Schedule, shall be guilty of an offence.

Pond survey to determine the presence of protected species, not only in the water but also in surrounding habitat, would be an important action in establishing protection of many ponds. Proceedings may be instigated by the local authority or by the police, taking into account advice from English Nature, and with the support of voluntary organisations such as Wildlife Trusts.

Tree Preservation Orders

Observation of aerial photography of farm ponds on Merseyside shows that many ponds are surrounded by trees. A farmer wishing to infill a pond in order to facilitate agricultural operations or to remove an attraction to trespassers will inevitably remove trees. There is thus potential scope for protection of ponds indirectly through protection of surrounding trees.

A tree preservation order (TPO) is an order made by a local planning authority in respect of trees, groups of trees or woodlands. The law relating to TPOs is found in Part 8 of the Town and Country Planning Act 1990, as amended by the Planning and Compensation Act 1991, and in numerous regulations issued under the planning acts. Under Section 198(1) of the 1990 Act, LPAs may make a TPO if it appears to them "expedient in the interests of amenity to make provision for the preservation" and advice in Department of the Environment Circular 36/78 states that TPOs "should be used to protect selected trees and woodlands if their removal would have a significant impact on the environment and its enjoyment by the public... The trees ... should therefore normally be visible from a public place". The advice goes on to state that other factors, such as importance as a wildlife habitat, may be taken into account.

There is thus scope for assessing those ponds where TPOs on surrounding trees would be justified under existing regulations and guidance.

The Hedgerow Regulations

Some farm ponds lie adjacent to hedgerows. The Hedgerow Regulations 1997 require a farmer to inform the LPA prior to the removal of any hedgerow, and the LPA can, if the hedgerow is important, refuse permission.

Protection is afforded to only a small proportion of hedgerows through the present Regulations, and the government is committed to reviewing the protection system in order to strengthen it (Griffiths, 1997). Due to limited LPA resources, most hedgerows will not be surveyed in advance; LPAs will survey and research hedgerows when applications for removal are received. However, it would be useful to survey and research in advance those hedgerows lying adjacent to important ponds in order to determine the level of protection the hedgerow, and indirectly the pond, can receive.

Designated Areas

Ponds that fall within statutorily or locally designated sites enjoy a limited degree of protection. Very few fall within Sites of Special Scientific Interest (SSSIs), although those that do are afforded protection under Section 29 of the Wildlife and Countryside Act.

Local Nature Reserves (LNRs) are also a statutory designation and, as they have no minimum size, could be applied to individual ponds if the interests on site were high in the local context; however, for designation the local authority must have a legal interest in the land, and this can restrict the applicability of the designation.

Many ponds fall within sites locally designated in Development Plans for nature conservation, heritage landscape, architectural conservation or Green Belt reasons. Several ponds are specifically designated as sites of local biological interest on botanical grounds within the Unitary Development Plans of all five local authorities on Merseyside. The degree of such protection is dependent upon the nature of the threat. If planning permission is not required, then these designations do not apply. LPAs are powerless to prevent many sites of local biological interest, for instance, being destroyed by owners ploughing or even bulldozing sites. However, if planning permission is required, the fact that a pond lies within a designated area gives the pond significant protection.

Planning conditions

Pond losses can occur due to temporary uses of land such as opencast coal mining or landfilling of waste. By use of planning conditions attached to planning permissions, both creation and management of ponds can be achieved. While this is relatively easy to achieve on mineral sites, and on sites subject to change of use, as in agriculture to golf courses, creation of water features on restored landfill sites is not encouraged by the Department of the Environment. Despite this, some landfill operators are having practical success in creating ecological water features on landfill sites (Barker, 1995).

Much more could be done through planning conditions. To maximise biodiversity objectives, it is suggested that a) retention of existing ponds, b) creation of new ponds and c) pond management should be the priorities, in declining order.

Planning obligations

Long term management of ponds can be achieved through planning obligations (comprising both planning agreements and unilateral undertakings) facilitated by Section 106 of the Town and Country Planning Act 1990 as substituted by Section 12(1) of the Planning and Compensation Act 1991. Bennett (1996) gives examples of the use of these to achieve, *inter alia*, 25 year management of ponds on Merseyside, primarily on new golf course developments.

An important element of planning obligations described in Department of the Environment Circular 1/97, is the use of planning obligations to offset the loss of or impact on any resource present on the site prior to development. Moreover, the substitute need not be exact, although there should be some relationship between what is lost and what is offered. Creation of ponds to compensate for replacement of other natural features may well be appropriate. The Countryside Commission believes that scope to achieve more benefits for the countryside, including restoration and creation of ponds and wetland, can be achieved through the use of planning obligations (Anon, 1993).

Farm Business Tenancies - conservation clauses and Management Agreements

Landowners and managers are now more aware of the importance of sustainably managing their land. Some farmers are working with bodies such as the Farming and Wildlife Advisory Groups and County Wildlife Trusts to further the ends of conservation.

Nevertheless, some tenant farmers still destroy features of interest which the landowners wish to retain but cannot, as there is no relevant clause within the tenancy agreement. It has been demonstrated that the time of highest risk to features of the farmed landscape occurs when there is a change in occupancy (Marsden & Munton, 1991). The inclusion of conservation measures within tenancy agreements would thus be beneficial.

Modern farm business tenancies are established under the Agricultural Tenancies Act 1995, with the exception of those to which the Agricultural Holdings Act 1986 still applies. The 1995 Act, although dealing at length with physical improvements on farms, does not touch upon retention of farm features of conservation interest. However, The Royal Institution of Chartered Surveyors (RICS), which prepares many Farm Business Tenancy Agreements, intends to include in the second edition of its Guidance Notes for Farm Business Tenancies several conservation clauses (I.D. Baker, ARICS, personal communication, 1997). These clauses include the following.

"1. Taking into account the terms of this Agreement the character and situation of the Holding and all relevant circumstances, the Tenant will maintain a reasonable standard of husbandry both in terms of the system of farming and the quantity and quality of produce, and at the same time will keep the Holding in a condition which will enable such a standard to be maintained in the future.

2. In considering whether the standard of husbandry achieved by the Tenant is reasonable, regard will be had to the extent to which ... (i) watercourses, ponds, marshy areas and other wetland features are conserved and any maintenance work required is undertaken on a rotational basis in autumn and winter only ... (n) the Tenant ensures that farm staff and contractors are aware of the husbandry standards required and adopt recommended practices."

This explicit recognition that conservation and management is good husbandry is a major step forward.

It is also important to reward land managers for developing a more environmentally benign strategy. Longer term Farm Business Tenancies which offer a rent rebate in return for conservation work carried out as part of an integrated land management plan are being introduced by some bodies acting as landlord, including the National Trust and Ministry of Defence. The Royal Society for the Protection of Birds offers lower initial rents to allow conservation work to be carried out and entry into an agri-environment scheme (I.D. Baker, ARICS, personal communication, 1997). North West Water Limited has developed Integrated Land Use Management Plans for their major estates in the North West of England, through which it seeks to ensure through agreement that farming practices are compatible with maintenance of biological interest. In some cases, as in the West Pennine

Moors Estate (an area of 6,868 hectares), survey of ponds on the estate is identified as a specific issue (Anon, 1995).

Under Section 39 of the Wildlife and Countryside Act, a local authority can enter into a management agreement with the owner or occupier of land that could protect ponds and be enforceable by the authority. In practice, such agreements are rarely used, for reasons including cost and the need for consent, although less formal management agreements can also be used.

Pond retention and management would be greatly assisted by efforts to encourage the inclusion of conservation clauses in all tenancy agreements, to encourage farmers to enter into agri-environmental schemes and to reward tenants for adopting conservation measures in an integrated land management plan.

The need for specific planning protection

There is a surprising range of powers to protect and manage ponds. However, the application of these mechanisms is complex, responsibilities are shared by diverse bodies and numerous loopholes in the law exist. Given a) the established importance of ponds to the biodiversity, landscape and history of an area, b) the considerable pond destruction incurred in recent decades, and c) the complexity and incompleteness of existing protection mechanisms, it is appropriate for specific legal protection to be afforded to ponds.

It is illogical that planning permission and a water abstraction licence may be required to create a pond, while destruction of ponds continues uncontrolled due to lack of clarity within the complexity of planning, waste licensing and pollution control mechanisms.

The Hedgerow Regulations and Tree Preservation Order regulations present two very different models that could be used in deriving a model for pond preservation. A legal definition of a pond would be required, and this would need to encompass at least temporary (seasonally dry) ponds, ponds with permanent standing water (although water level may fluctuate), and ponds with and without inlet(s) and outlet(s). Criteria to assess the value of ponds would be required if the Hedgerow Regulations were used as the model.

Specific protection would not prevent the loss of ponds through insidious encroachment or compel farmers to carry out pond management. Indeed, the imposition of specific protection might lead to pre-emptive removal of ponds prior to regulations coming into force, as has been personally observed with the introduction of hedgerow regulations. Furthermore, pond retention can also be achieved by improved funding regimes for pond management. Increased funding for both creation and management of ponds is essential.

Nevertheless, specific protection of ponds through the planning process would complement such measures for pond creation and management. It would also bring forcibly to the attention of those who have thoughtlessly destroyed so many ponds in the past the importance attached by the general public to the retention in the future of these important features of the countryside.

General references

Anon. (1993) *Countryside benefits from planning obligations. Countryside Planning Statement. CCP440,* Countryside Commission: Cheltenham.

Anon. (1995) *Integrated Land Use Management Plan for West Pennine Moors Estate,* unpublished management plan produced by North West Water Limited.

Barker, C. (1995) The creation of wetland habitats on landfill sites. *Waste Planning* **16:** 9-13.

Bennett, C.M. (1996) Achieving ecological management of golf courses through legal mechanisms. *Aspects of Applied Biology* **44:** 481-486.

Griffiths, B. (1997) Hedgerow law is to be revamped. *Planning* **1221:** 1, 5

Marsden, T.K. & Munton, R.J.C. (1991) The farmed landscape and the occupancy change process. *Environment and Planning A,* **23:** 663-676.

Legislative references (all published by HMSO: London)

Wildlife and Countryside Act 1981.

Town and Country Planning Act 1990.

Environmental Protection Act 1990.

Planning and Compensation Act 1991.

Water Resources Act 1991.

The Waste Management Licensing Regulations 1994. Statutory Instrument 1994 No. 1056.

The Town and Country Planning (General Permitted Development) Order 1995. Statutory Instrument 1995 No. 418.

The Town and Country Planning (General Development Procedure) Order 1995. Statutory Instrument 1995 No. 419.

Environment Act 1995.

Agricultural Tenancies Act 1995.

Planning Obligations. Department of the Environment Circular 1/97.

The Hedgerow Regulations 1997. Statutory Instrument 1997 No. 1160.

An economic evaluation of farmland ponds: environmental values and the potential for income generation and diversification

C. Baker

Liverpool John Moores University, School of Social Science,
Trueman Building ,15-21 Webster Street, Liverpool, L3 2ET
c.baker@livjm.ac.uk

Background information

In the market-place, the individual has fairly clear information on which to base valuation and choices. The product tends to be visible, its characteristics are generally well known, and it has a market price. The individual, on the basis of the available information, weighs up quantity, quality and price on offer. These preferences are translated into market behaviour which contributes to a market outcome in terms of production and consumption. Conversely however it is often the case that environmental goods and services have no market price tag and a considerable amount of uncertainty can surround their true value and significance (Turner *et al.*, 1994). Many of these environmental assets are also public goods and this is another characteristic that makes it difficult for markets in such assets to evolve. The public good is special in that its benefits are available to a group for simultaneous consumption. In order to make comparisons involving an unpriced good or service, it is necessary to impute a value as otherwise none will be available. Even where some prices are available it may be the case that these fail to encapsulate all of the value that surrounds a key environmental asset. Again imputing a value can be justified and will assist in moving towards socially satisfactory outcomes for environmental assets.

Environmental economics has gone a considerable way towards a classification of economic values as they relate to natural environments (Turner *et al.*, 1994). The terminology is still not fully agreed, but the approach is based on the traditional explanation of how value occurs (i.e. it is based on the interaction between a human subject, the valuer, and objects - things to be valued). Individuals have a number of held values which in turn result in objects being given various assigned values. In order, in principle, to arrive at an aggregate measure of value (total economic value) there is a need to identify user values and non-user values.

By definition user values derive from the actual use of the environment and involve observable willingness to pay for use and access, as is demonstrated by land rentals and entrance charges. Slightly more complex are values expressed through options to use the environment (option values) in the future. They are essentially expressions of preference (willingness to pay) for the conservation of the environmental systems or components of systems against some probability that the individual will make use of them at a later date.

Non-use values are more problematic. They suggest non-instrumental values which are in the real nature of the thing but unassociated with actual use, or even the option to use the thing. Instead, such values are taken to be entities that reflect people's preferences, but include concern for, sympathy with, and respect for the rights or welfare of non-human life forms.. These values are still anthropocentric but may include a recognition of the value of the very existence of certain species or of whole ecosystems. The values referred to here are necessarily fuzzy values (Pearce *et al.*, 1989). It is not very clear how these values are best defined or measured. Although it is clear that the concept of existence value should not include vicarious benefits such as the bequest value which is a form of option value involving the gifting of environmental assets between generations.

To summarise then: *Total economic value is made up of actual use value plus option value plus existence value*. (Pearce *et al.*, 1989).

A number of different approaches exist to enable the valuation of environmental attributes be they landscapes, sites or endangered species. The appropriateness or relevance of particular techniques will depend upon the nature of the problem and the ease with which particular types of information can be generated. The replacement cost technique looks at the cost of replacing or restoring a damaged asset and uses this cost as a measure of the benefit of restoration. For example, where wetlands have been heavily depleted, replacement costs (wetland restoration, relocation or new wetland creation) might be allowable as a first approximation of the benefits of future wetland conservation, or wetland loss.

In the opportunity cost approach no direct attempt is made to value environmental benefits. Instead, the benefits of the activity causing environmental degradation - the filling in of a pond, for example - are estimated in order to set a benchmark for what the environmental benefits would have to be for the development (in this case, agriculture) *not* to be worthwhile. This is not a valuation technique per se, but it allows decision-makers to focus on the values involved. For example, much of the recent loss of European wetlands due to the operation of the Common Agricultural Policy represents a socially inefficient result because of the heavily subsidised nature of the drainage investments and arable crops that replaced the wetland. Conservation would not have involved particularly high opportunity costs.

The challenge of directly valuing the environmental good is now however increasingly being accepted. For example landscape valuation in the Yorkshire Dales National Park (Willis & Garrod, 1993). Various direct valuation methods are available, the hedonistic price method (**HPM**), travel cost method (**TCM**) and the contingent valuation method (**CVM**). The HPM and the TCM methods are based on revealed preferences for the environment, whereas CVM is based on expressed preferences for the environment.

In HPM variations in land or house prices are used to establish the value of environmental attributes that are intrinsic to a type of land or a particular site. The method is necessarily statistical. A study of house prices conducted in Gloucestershire showed that the presence of open water close to a house had no observable effect, marshland a negative effect and woodland a positive influence (Garrod and Willis, 1992). The preferences measured here are not directly transferable to small water bodies in an agricultural landscape. It also remains to be seen if other rural areas show similar effects on house prices after standardising for water quality.

TCM recognises that visitors making recreational journeys have user costs particularly the direct cost of travel by public or private transport. Thus users of a national park or a beauty

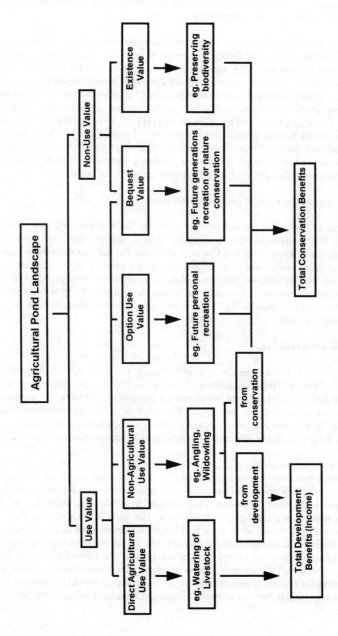

Figure 1: Valuing the agricultural pond landscape   (after Turner et al., 1994)

spot demonstrate that they value the protected land by incurring considerable access costs which are measurable and can be aggregated.

CVM is something of a breakthrough in environmental valuation. It has been suggested (Willis and Garrod, 1993) that CVM has opened up new ways of measuring commodities, including landscape and previously unmeasurable quantities such as the option and existence value for wildlife. CVM is an extension of attitude and preference measurement techniques employed by psychologists and other social researchers. Essentially respondents are asked in an interview situation to express their willingness to pay for particular environmental outcomes. For example to protect a threatened village pond. Pearce (1989) gives an explanation of best practice in CVM. Willis and Garrod (1993) used CVM to discover the value of different landscape types in the Yorkshire Dales National Park. CVM studies have tended to establish that existence values are a significant element of total economic value a finding which presumably would apply to amphibian and pond conservation.

Economic approaches to pond protection and management.

The loss of farmland ponds in North West England has now been well documented (see for example Boothby *et al.*, 1995). The challenge is to develop and implement a conservation model for farmland ponds in the region which recognises that the vast majority of these small water bodies lie on private land. One approach is via the involvement of local communities and the 'Pond Warden' scheme. Another approach is to tackle the economics of pond loss via the landholders themselves. Presenting an economic argument for pond protection and management may have longer lasting implications for the resource, which was initially created by agricultural practices.

Valuing the pond resource.

Since the mid 1980s extensive use of monetary valuation methods has led to the publication of a large literature consisting of a wide diversity of case studies many of which have had a significant impact upon environmental protection. To date, no such literature relates to small water bodies in the agricultural landscape. However there is no reason to suppose that an economic evaluation would not yield significant results in terms of use and non use values. Figure 1 indicates the various sources of value that a study needs to consider.

Small water bodies are part of a lowland landscape in counties like Cheshire and evidence from landscape evaluation studies shows the public can have a high regard for landscapes that they favour. It is likely that public appreciation of landscape types will produce a rank order of landscape preferences. National Park designation in the UK suggests that upland landscapes will on average achieve higher rank, but pond landscapes are likely to be appreciated and even preferred to some agricultural landscapes such as those produced by arable production. Additionally conservation of ponds would tap into a regard for species. A CVM study by (Semples *et al.*, 1986) revealed average non use values for Bighorn Sheep of $7 amongst a range of species and natural amenities. Amphibians should produce at least comparable results in terms of existence values. While ecological education can never be taken for granted it is plausible that appreciation of ponds and amphibians will correlate well.

Income generation and diversification.

Farmland ponds owe their existence to agricultural practices such as marling and were also used to water livestock. These use values were in their time more than enough to guarantee that farmers would protect and manage the pond resource. Today however such privately owned and managed environmental assets are not easy to justify in commercial terms. New use values need to be developed and fostered as part of a conservation strategy. Such a conservation strategy would have the advantage of being self organising and self financing. Additionally, if non use values could be confirmed it would perhaps be possible to justify a share of public sector environmental funding.

Consideration needs to be given to the potential that small water bodies have to generate income for farmers allowing some diversification away from core farm businesses. New use values such as angling, wildfowling and nature trails could subject to the constraints of local markets be developed. Willingness to pay for leisure activities is well demonstrated and there is no reason in principle why some farmers could not participate in what might become secure small businesses based on the management of environmental assets. In developing uses such as angling and wildfowling it is likely that particular ecologies are going to be favoured. However providing the changes concerned are part of a package of pond management measures these should be supported as innovative changes which can help to sustain agricultural pond landscapes into the next millennium.

References

Boothby, J. Hull, A.P. & Jeffreys, D.A. (1995) Sustaining a threatened landscape: ponds in Cheshire. *Journal of Environmental Planning and Management, 38: 561-568.*

Garrod, G.D. and Willis, K.G. (1992) Valuing goods' characteristics: an application of the Hedonic Price Method to environmental attributes. *Journal of Environmental Planning and Management, 34: 59-76.*

Pearce, D., Markandya, A., Barbier, E.B. (1989) *Blueprint for a Green Economy.* Earthscan Publications Ltd, London.

Semples, K, Gowen, M, and Dixon, J. (1986) The validity of the Contingent Valuation Method for estimating non-use components of preservation values for unique natural resources. *Paper presented to the American Agricultural Economics Association, Reno, July 1986.*

Turner, K.R., Pearce, D. and Bateman, I. (1994) *Environmental Economics: An elementary introduction.* Harvester Wheatsheaf, London.

Willis, K.G. and Garrod, G.D. (1993) Valuing landscape: a Contingent Valuation approach. *Journal of Environmental Planning and Management,* **37:** 1-22.

Geographical Information Systems (GIS) in the Pond *Life* Project.

J.M. Bloor

Pond *Life* Project, Liverpool John Moores University,
15-21 Webster St., Liverpool L3 2ET
email: j.m.bloor@livjm.ac.uk

Introduction

Geographical Information Systems (GIS) have formed an integral part of many conservation projects, especially in the measurement of landscape change (see, for example, Haines-Young *et al.*, 1994). The constantly shifting patterns of a landscape mean that effective monitoring requires a dynamic system which can be updated for strategic purposes. In the Pond *Life* Project, GIS is playing a central role in habitat recording, data management, strategic planning, and general communication of results.

Within the Pond *Life* Project most of the partners have access to and utilise GIS. In Belgium, Project staff using GIS to examine movement between breeding ponds, foraging ponds and the wider landscape; in The Netherlands, GIS is being used in a predictive fashion for designating new pond location (Vos, 1993).

GIS in North West England.

In the home project area, GIS is used, *inter alia*, for the following purposes:

recording locations of ponds and other small water-bodies;

carrying out audits of the pond resource, rates and causes of loss, locational patterns, and referring this to local authority boundaries;

using GIS modelling capabilities for designating areas of 'core pondscape';

relating pond-loss to the core pondscape, identifying pondscape change and fragmentation, and investigating strategic changes;

keeping track of volunteers and local surveys;

structuring the large biological data base deriving from detailed pond surveys;

presenting the results of these analyses.

Figure 1 shows the general structure of the GIS.

Figure 1:   **General structure of the GIS**

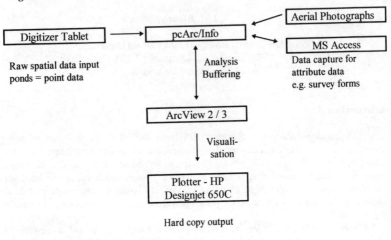

Raw spatial data input
ponds = point data

Hard copy output

<u>Equipment</u>

The GIS is run on several stand-alone PC's (pentium 166, 32Mb ram) which have access to digitizers and plotters. The core software elements are ESRI's pcArc/Info 3.4.2 and ArcView 3.0 (provided under the academic-network CHEST system); this system is underpinned by a dBASE relational database, which can import/export from a variety of compatible systems. Much of the biological survey data are held within Microsoft Access 2.0, all of which reside on a Windows 3.11 platform. (see Figure 1). ArcView 3.0 is also used running under Windows '95.

Information issues

The GIS uses spatial data (pond locations, local government boundaries, grid-lines, etc.) which are obtained from Ordnance Survey under licence via co-operation with various local authorities. Pond locations, but not the ponds themselves, were taken from 1:10,000 / 1:10,560 OS sheets. A considerable amount of value-added data, often of a summary nature, has been generated from the GIS using its modelling capability. Ecological data derives from a number of sources, including professional surveys carried out as part of the project, volunteer reports, data exchanges with other organisations. Summary, more generalised status information on ponds has been obtained from aerial photographs.

The quality of the data is variable. Volunteers do not generally have the same expertise as the professional ecologist. Most volunteers' reports confirm only the presence or absence of a pond, anything more is seen as a bonus. The detailed surveys (c. 1000 to date) are in-depth studies carried out by professional ecologists, recording

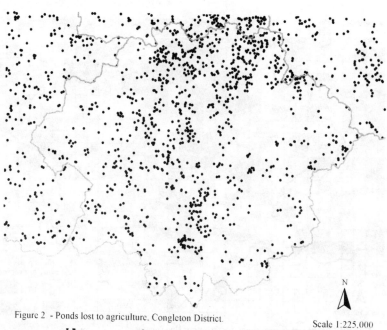

Figure 2 - Ponds lost to agriculture, Congleton District.

Scale 1:225,000

Figure 3 - Ponds lost to non - agricultural uses, Congleton District.

Scale 1:225,000

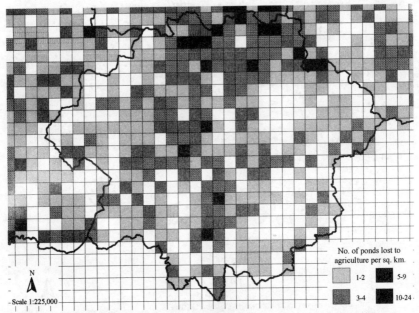

No. of ponds lost to
agriculture per sq. km.

1-2	5-9
3-4	10-24

Scale 1:225,000

Figure 4 - Ponds lost to agriculture, vectorization 1km squares.

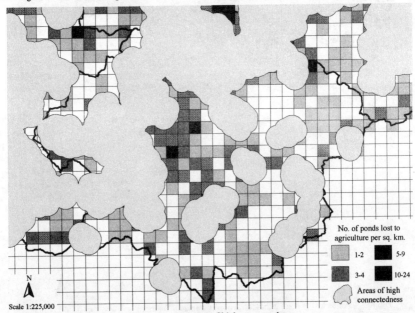

No. of ponds lost to
agriculture per sq. km.

1-2	5-9
3-4	10-24

Areas of high
connectedness

Scale 1:225,000

Figure 5 - Ponds lost to agriculture, showing areas of high connectedness.

detailed information on the flora and fauna of the pond, the surrounding terrestrial matrix (especially the 'buffer zone'), pH, conductivity, and usage.

The major problem with any data collection exercise which gathers such a wide variety of information is the design of the database. Initially it was hoped that one database would suffice for all the data received, however as the project progressed it became apparent that the difference in survey forms and the knowledge base of the surveyors has meant producing several databases, one for each major category of surveyor. This still allows the attribute data to be related spatially to the ponds held on the GIS, but means that there is a wide range of information detail.

Another problem with surveyed information is variable accuracy in recording the grid reference of a pond. Given the density of ponds in some areas, it is necessary to obtain 6 + 6 figure references, in order to match survey information with pond locations (recorded only as an approximate centroid). Grid referencing without such accuracy could mean the pond surveyed is one of up to 20 ponds lying within 'search radius' of the real site. After experimentation, we now ask volunteers to record information to a 'real' section of map rather than simply quoting a grid reference. Even this however has its difficulties.

We estimate that the recording of pond sites was made with a high order of accuracy, but that interference is caused by several factors inherent in the base-mapping:

- changing definitions of small water bodies
- variable representations of ponds as pond/ marsh/ rough ground
- time of survey (summer/ winter/ periodic drought)
- errors carried forward from earlier mappings

Pond representation

The representation of a pond by a point has obvious disadvantages. Mechanically, there are significant problems in portraying such small objects when preparing a map of an entire county (16,000 ponds) or even of a District: even when mapping at fairly high resolutions, it is difficult to show every pond (Figure 2 & 3). Yet for obvious reasons, the project is concerned with individual ponds and thus a discrete representation is necessary. However, it is possible to convert discrete point data to grid squares or even to generate a rasterized cover (Figure 4 & 5); this, of course, involves some loss both of precision and of information content, though the resulting portrayal can be extremely useful especially where targeting of Project actions is concerned.

Pondscape

In order to combat the mechanical problems of point representation, use has been made of a model of "pondscape", in which areas of high pond density are delineated by reference to local average values. This enables us to draw maps of 'core' areas (for synoptic purposes, for strategic views, or even for biodiversity planning) without individual ponds being shown (see Boothby, *this volume*). Though the definition of appropriate local average values is subject to debate, such maps provide accurate delineations of core landscape free from the problems introduced by analysis based on the 'false boundaries' of a grid square system.

References

Boothby, J., Hull, A.P. & Jeffreys, D.A. (1995) Sustaining a threatened landscape: farmland ponds in Cheshire. *Journal of Environmental Planning and Management,* 38: 561-568.

Haines-Young, R., Green, D.R., & Cousins S.H. (1994) *Landscape Ecology and Geographical Information Systems.* Taylor & Francis, London.

Vos, C.C. (1993) *Versnippering en landinrichting in Zeeuws-Vlaanderen,* IBN-DLO, Wageningen.

Species records in the biodiversity surveys of the Pond *Life* Project.

J. Boothby

Pond *Life* Project, Liverpool John Moores University,
15-21 Webster St., Liverpool L3 2ET

Introduction

Full analysis of the detailed biodiversity surveys (n = 750) generated by the Pond *Life* Project is underway as a long-term investogation and will focus on inter-species relationships, the role of the proximate terrestrial environment, spatial components of species' populations, and the relationship between species, environment and the wider pondscape. This appendix summarises the survey findings to date (based on c.500 surveys from 1995 and 1996) from the perspectives of (i) rare species and (ii) significant additions to regional records.

All survey work was carried out by Jonathan Guest Ecological Surveys and reported in Pond L*ife* Project (1996; 1997) from where these data are derived (and see Guest, *this volume*). Assistance in identification was provided by Dr Garth Foster (water beetles), John Bratton (JNCC: reed beetles), Dr Michael Kerney (Natural History Museum: molluscs). Assistance was also provided by Martin Drake (English Nature), Deborah Procter (JNCC), Steve Garland and staff (Bolton Museum Biological Records Centre). Farmers and landowners kindly gave permission for access and survey.

Vegetation

Nationally "Scarce" species were recorded at the following number of sites in Cheshire (C), Lancashire (L), Wigan (Wg) and Wirral (Wi) - see Table 1.

Table 1:   Records for Nationally Scarce vegetation species.

Callitriche hermaphroditica	*Autumnal Starwort	1 L (unconfirmed)
Carex elata	*Tufted Sedge	1 C
Ceratophyllum submersum	*Soft Hornwort	1 C
Cicuta virosa	Cowbane	19 C
Cyperus longus	Galingale	1 Wg
Hydrocharis morsus-ranae	*Frogbit	3 C
Nymphoides peltata	Fringed water-lily	5 *C*
Stratiotes aloides	Water-soldier	1C 3Wi 1Wg 5L

*   Not classified as Scarce by Stewart *et al.* (1994)

Invertebrates

A total of 34 species with an official JNCC scarcity Status was found. These are listed below in Table 2.

Table 2: Invertebrates - Endangered, Vulnerable and Notable species found.

Endangered RDB1	Vulnerable RDB2	Notable A
Hydrochara caraboides	*Lymnaea glabra*	*Dytiscus circumcinctus*

Notable B

Noterus crassicornis	*Hydroglyphus geminus*	*Hydraena testacea*
Dytiscus circumflexus	*Cercyon convexiusculus*	*Ochthebius exsculptus*
Hydaticus seminiger	*Cercyon obsoletus (=lugubris)*	*Ochthebius viridis*
Rhantus suturalis	*Cercyon sternalis*	*Donacia clavipes*
Agabus chalconatus	*Cercyon tristis*	*Plateumaris affinis*
Agabus unguicularis	*Cercyon ustulatus*	*Cyphon pubescens*
Ilybius fenestratus	*Enochus melanocephalus*	
Ilybius guttiger	*Enochus ochropterus*	
Ilybius subaeneus	*Helochares lividus*	
Hydroporus neglectus	*Helochares punctatus*	

Regionally Notable

Donacia vulgaris	*Leptocerus tineiformis*	*Anax imperator*
Cymatia coleoptera	*Notonecta marmorea viridis*	

Great Crested Newt (Triturus cristatus)

The records for the Great Crested Newt suggest a geographical extension to the recorded presence of this species, though extant atlas maps (Arnold, 1995) are known to be deficient. North of the Mersey, the survey has produced two new 10 km square records, one in the Lune Valley [SD57], the other in the Ribble estuary [SD42]. In Cheshire, 8 such new squares were identified: SJ46; SJ47; SJ54; SJ55; SJ56; SJ57; SJ64; and SJ77 which were previously not recorded". Further records were located in two squares for which only pre-1969 records existed: SJ66 and SJ76. The distribution map for the species in Cheshire no longer shows a blank across the centre of the county.

Bird data

The presence of certain species is significant for ponds. The Mute Swan, Canada Goose, and Coot are implicated in the decline of pond vegetation, grazing submerged pond weed (Rodwell, 1995) and emergent vegetation. There may also be effects on turbidity and photosynthesis. Where tame waterfowl are fed, or rearing takes place, weed-grazing, an increase in turbidity, and faecal accumulation can have marked, negative effects upon life in the pond.

Though ponds are not widely perceived as important bird habitat, the following records (Table3) are worth reporting. The survey was not primarily intended to effect comprehensive recording of bird species and only significant presence was noted, especially in respect of land-birds.

Table 3: Bird species recorded on pre-prepared checklist and in 'Significant Notes' at survey.

Checklist		Noted	
Acrocephalus schoenobaenus	Sedge Warbler	*Acrocephalus scirpaceus*	Reed warbler
Alcedo atthis	Kingfisher	*Columba oenas*	Stock Dove
Anas platyrhyncus	Mallard	*Gallinago gallinago*	Snipe
Ardea cinerea	Heron	*Haematopus ostralegus*	Oystercatcher
Athene noctua	Little Owl		
Branta canadensis	Canada Goose	*Numenius arquata*	Curlew
Cygnus olor	Mute Swan	*Riparia riparia*	Sand Martin
Dendrocopos major	Gr. Spotted Woodpecker	*Tadorna tadorna*	Shelduck
Dendrocopos minor	Lr. Spotted Woodpecker	*Tringa ochropus*	Green Sandpiper
Emberiza schoeniclus	Reed Bunting		
Fulica atra	Coot	*Tringa totanus*	Redshank
Gallinula chloropus	Moorhen		
Sylvia curruca	Lesser Whitethroat		
Tachybaptus ruficollis	Little Grebe		

References.

Arnold, H,R. (1995) *Atlas of amphibians and reptiles in Britain.* Natural Environment Research Council, Huntingdon.

Pond *Life* Project (1996) *Critical pond biodiversity survey 1995.* Pond *Life* Project (unpublished).

Pond *Life* Project   **(1997)** *Critical pond biodiversity survey 1996.*   Pond *Life* Project (unpublished).

Rodwell, J.S. (ed) (1995)   *British plant Communities: Vol 4: Aquatic coomunities, swamps, and tall-herb fens.*   Cambridge University Press, Cambridge.

Stewart, A., Pearman, D.A. & Preston, C.D. (eds)   **(1994)**   *Scarce plants in Britain.* JNCC, Peterborough.

Species turnover in Peak District dewponds - metapopulation implications for pond conservation

R.A.Briers

Department of Animal and Plant Sciences, University of Sheffield,
Sheffield, S. Yorks, S10 2TN, UK

Introduction

Species turnover (the extinction and recolonisation of local populations within habitat fragments) has been an important issue in ecology since MacArthur & Wilson first put forward the theory of island biogeography (MacArthur & Wilson, 1967). Attention has been re-focused on the process of species turnover with the development of metapopulation theory (reviews in Gilpin & Hanski, 1991; Hanski & Gilpin, 1996), where regional persistence of a species is seen as a result of a balance of colonisation and extinction in a system of semi-independent populations linked by dispersal.

Ponds are isolated waterbodies which form discrete habitat patches. Taxa may move between ponds via dispersal (active or passive) and many species found in ponds are well adapted to dispersal. Consequently new ponds rapidly accumulate species (Barnes, 1983; Layton & Voshell, 1991). However the species complement is not constant; turnover may occur due to extinction and subsequent recolonisation after initial colonisation (Barnes, 1983). This combination of natural habitat fragmentation and species dispersal means that pond systems may be good examples of field metapopulations (see, for example Jeffries, 1994). However habitat suitability may also influence pond occupancy (Friday, 1987), imposing a more deterministic pattern of distribution than would predicted solely from colonisation and extinction.

This study examines turnover of two species of mobile hemipterans (water-bugs): *Notonecta maculata* Fabricius and *Corixa punctata* (Illiger) over a four year period. Both of these species are strong fliers (Walton, 1935; Popham, 1964) and hence are likely to actively disperse between ponds. The study was carried out in thirty-one small man-made ponds known as dewponds in the Peak National Park, Derbyshire (National Grid Reference of study area SK 1168 to 2380). Dewponds are largely found in calcareous areas where there is little natural standing water. Originally constructed to provide drinking water for livestock, dewponds have declined in many areas due to neglect and replacement by modern cattle troughs. Dewponds were traditionally constructed with a lining of impermeable clay into which limestone or flint pitchers were embedded to protect the lining from stock trampling (Hayfield and Brough, 1987). A more recent construction method is to line the pond with concrete. In the Peak District, dewponds are only found on the calcareous White Peak area and are still fairly abundant. They support moderately diverse invertebrate communities and vegetation is generally sparse, with low diversity in most ponds (Warren *et al.*, 1997).

Methods

The data analysed here come from two surveys of dewponds. The first was carried out in July 1992 (Warren *et al.*, 1997) and the second in July 1996 (R.A.Briers, *unpublished*). The former study used a three minute pond net sweep to sample the ponds. In the 1996 survey a seine-type net was used for sampling. Differences between the sampling methods are unlikely to have affected the results (R.A.Briers, *unpublished data*); the species chosen for study were locally (within ponds) and regionally (over the study area) abundant in both years, reducing the likelihood of pseudoturnover being recorded as a result of sampling errors. In addition to recording pond occupancy, a range of environmental characteristics (pond basin and wetted width, maximum mud depth and percentage cover, pH, conductivity, Secchi disc depth and macrophyte species and percentage cover) were recorded for all the ponds in both years.

Results

Occupancy and turnover

Pond occupancy and population turnover between 1992 and 1996 are summarised in Table 1. The proportion of ponds occupied in each year was fairly constant for both species, although *N. maculata* underwent a slight decline. Turnover rates were high in the four year period between surveys, suggesting that colonisation and extinction are important components of regional population dynamics. There was no significant association between the turnover of the two species ($\chi^2 = 0.1$, df. $= 2$, $p > 0.05$). The distribution of occupied and vacant ponds for both species in 1992 and 1996 is shown in Figures 1 and 2.

Table 1. Occupancy and turnover of populations in dewponds 1992-1996.

Species	Occupancy		Colonisations	Extinctions
	1992	1996		
N. maculata	18	13	4	9
C. punctata	22	21	6	7

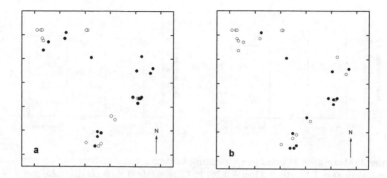

Figure 1. Map of dewponds surveyed, showing changes in distribution of *N. maculata*, a) 1992 b) 1996. Axis units = 2km, open symbols = vacant, solid symbols = occupied. Size of ponds not shown to scale.

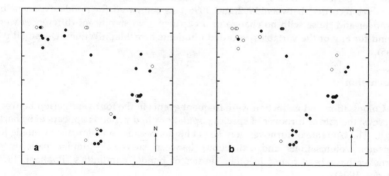

Figure 2. Map of dewponds surveyed, showing changes in distribution of *C. punctata*, a) 1992 b) 1996. Axis units and symbols as in Figure 1.

Turnover and pond area

Species turnover was analysed with respect to pond area. For both *N. maculata* and *C. punctata* there was no significant difference between the area of ponds experiencing turnover and those with no change in status (Figure 3).

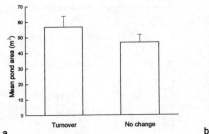 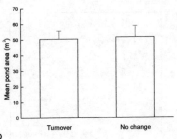

a   b

Figure 3. Mean area of ponds experiencing turnover or no change in occupancy, a) *N. maculata*, (t = 1.17, df. = 23, p = 0.25) b) *C. punctata* (t = -0.12, df. = 23, p = 0.90). Error bars = 1 standard error.

Turnover and habitat change

Species turnover was also analysed in relation to changes in pond habitat in the four year period between surveys. The mean absolute change in each of the habitat variables recorded between 1992 and 1996 was compared for ponds experiencing turnover and those with no change in occupancy. No significant differences were found for any of the variables recorded (Students t- or Mann Witney U-test, all p > 0.05).

Discussion

Colonisation and extinction were frequent events in the four year period between surveys; the rate of turnover of species populations in dewponds appears to be fairly high. The true rate of turnover may be yet higher because no allowance is made for repeated colonisations and extinctions between surveys. Similar patterns of turnover have been found in other studies of pond communities (Popham, 1951; Jeffries, 1994).

If no assumptions are made about the suitability of habitat, turnover may be expected to occur more often in small ponds. Maximum population size is generally limited by habitat patch size and hence small ponds can only support small populations, which are more vulnerable to extinction as a result of demographic variation (Williamson, 1981; Hanski, 1994). However there is no evidence that turnover is more frequent in smaller ponds for either species.

Turnover may also occur due to changes in the habitat of ponds between the surveys. This may affect the suitability of individual ponds for the species in question. Again there is no evidence in this study for turnover driven by habitat change. Although species precise habitat requirements are poorly known in many cases, for the species considered in this study, turnover appears to be largely stochastic. The strong 'element of chance' in the composition of pond communities (Talling, 1951; Jeffries 1989) may be in part due to the dynamics of colonisation and extinction that are fundamental to species persistence at the metapopulation level.

Metapopulation dynamics may be important in determining the occurrence of species in ponds, at least the mobile species capable of dispersal, and this has implications for pond conservation. Given that species may come and go from ponds due to stochastic extinction and recolonisation, the absence of a species in a particular year may not necessarily indicate that the habitat is poor or unsuitable. Assessment of conservation value is often based on single surveys which may not give true representation of the fauna supported.

If metapopulation dynamics are important within pond communities then persistence of species over a regional area may require a network of 'suitable' sites. This would suggest a change of focus for pond conservation strategies moving away from management of sites in isolation and towards maintenance of systems of ponds over a regional area. Other authors (Boothby & Hull, 1995; Williams *et al.*, 1997) have also highlighted this broader view of pond conservation, emphasising the need for the conservation of viable 'pondscape' over a regional area.

Acknowledgements

I would like to thank Phil Warren for discussion and comments on the manuscript and the landowners and farmers in the study area for allowing access to their ponds.

References

Barnes, L.E. (1983) The colonisation of ball-clay ponds by macroinvertebrates and macrophytes. *Freshwater Biology* 13: 561-578

Boothby, J. & Hull, A.P. (1995) Restoring and rehabilitating pond landscapes: thinking strategically. Griffiths, G.H. (Ed.) *Landscape ecology: theory and application*, IALE (UK) 4th Annual Conference, Reading, 186-189

Friday, L.E. (1987) The diversity of macroinvertebrate and macrophyte communities in ponds. *Freshwater Biology* 18: 87-104

Gilpin, M.E. & Hanski, I. (Eds.) (1991) *Metapopulation dynamics: empirical and theoretical investigations*, Academic Press, London.

Hanski, I. (1994) Patch-occupancy dynamics in fragmented landscapes. *Trends in Ecology and Evolution* 9: 131-135

Hanski, I. & Gilpin, M.E. (Eds.) (1996) *Metapopulation biology: ecology, genetics and evolution*, Academic Press, London.

Hayfield, C. & Brough, M. (1987) Dewponds and pondmakers of the Yorkshire Wolds. *Folk Life* 25: 74-91

Jeffries, M. (1989) Measuring Talling's 'element of chance in pond populations'. *Freshwater Biology* **21**: 383-393

Jeffries, M. (1994) Invertebrate communities and turnover in wetland ponds affected by drought. *Freshwater Biology* **32**: 603-612

Layton, R.J. & Voshell, J.R. (1991) Colonisation of new experimental ponds by benthic macroinvertebrates. *Environmental Entomology* **20**: 110-117

MacArthur, R.H. & Wilson, E.O. (1967) *The Theory of Island Biogeography*, Princeton University Press, Princeton, NJ.

Popham, E.J. (1951) A study of the changes of the water bug fauna of North Surrey from 1946 to 1950 with special reference to the migration of corixids. *Journal of the Society for British Entomology* **3**: 268-273

Popham, E.J. (1964) The migration of aquatic bugs with special reference to the Corixidae (Hemiptera Heteroptera). *Archiv für Hydrobiologie* **60**: 450-496

Talling, J.F. (1951) The element of chance in pond populations. *The Naturalist* **1951**: 157-170

Walton, G.A. (1935) Field experiments on the flight of *Notonecta maculata* Fabr. (Hemipt.). *Transactions of the Society for British Entomology* **2**: 137-144

Warren, P.; Rotherham, I.; Eades, P.; Wright, S. & Howe, P. (1997) Invertebrate and macrophyte communities of dewponds in the Peak District, with particular reference to the method of pond construction. *Journal of Peak District Natural History and Archaeology* **1**: *in press*

Williams, P.; Biggs, J.; Corfield, A.; Fox, G.; Walker, D. & Whitfield, M. (1997) Designing new ponds for wildlife. *British Wildlife* **8**: 137-150

Williamson, M. (1981) *Island Populations*. Oxford University Press, Oxford.

Local Community Pond Survey in 47 Cambridge Green Belt rural parishes

Sharon Hearle

Cambridge Green Belt Project, Enterprise House, Maris Lane, Trumpington, Cambridge CB2 2LE

Abstract

The survey work by volunteers was a search for old and new ponds in 47 rural parishes around Cambridge. The specific involvement of local people raised awareness about ponds generally and encouraged the creation of new ponds. Many memories and stories about old ponds were collected and compiled in a booklet called "Discovering Ponds Around Cambridge". The surveyors were able to identify many landowners which makes targeting of grants schemes and other resources more effective.

The survey results were recorded on a database. A simple grading scheme to provide some assessment of the pond resource was devised and to help to set priorities for further detailed survey and mangement.
Results indicated an interesting distribution of ponds. There were several parishes with only one or two ponds and others with over 12. It was particularly difficult to define the importance of any one pond over another in the context of such a broad survey. Nearly one-third of the remaining ponds surveyed were dry, full of rubbish or totally shaded by trees.

Background

The Survey of Landscape Change by Cambridgeshire County Council (1994) indicated that 11% of ponds had disappeared in three sample areas of the county between 1985 and 1994. This loss is on top of large losses since the turn of the century and is a worrying trend. There was no information available on the pond resource in the Cambridge Green Belt Area. A survey would help to plan how future resources should be targeted to increase and improve the pond habitat.

The survey took place between March and October 1996 and covered 47 rural parishes around Cambridge. There was no inventory to begin with but an early estimate suggested there might be over 300 ponds. Resources for the survey were very limited and all site survey work and information gathering was done by volunteers with support from the Cambridge Green Belt Project Officer.

A pond was defined as a water body less than 100 metres square. This type of measurement can be difficult and a list of 'lakes' not included in the survey as ponds was made. Some apparent ponds are actually enlarged sections of streams.

Methods

The first action was to draw up a list of potential ponds in each of the 47 parishes to survey. All potential ponds shown in blue on the current Ordnance Survey Pathfinder Series were listed. These maps are based on large scale surveys done between 1964 and 1983. It was not possible to know what state particular ponds were in and it is assumed that the blue colour indicated that the pond held water. Known new ponds and any others not marked on OS maps were added to the list. Small garden ponds were not included. The garden pond was difficult to exclude because many old farm ponds are now part of gardens.

Local Contacts

A letter with a parish map showing all ponds was sent to all the parish councils in the area requesting information about the ponds and in particular land ownership. An appeal for volunteer surveyors was launched via newspaper features and parish magazines. There were three training/volunteer support days in basic pond survey not including invertebrates. A leaflet and simple survey form were designed and printed for volunteers to use in the field. Fourteen different volunteers took part in the survey although many other people provided information.

Pond Grading Scheme

It was decided that a grading scheme however crude would help to come up with some estimation of the quality of the remaining pond resource and to plan future work. This is demonstrated in Table 1.

Table 1: The Grading Scheme

Grade	Description
One	High Wildlife Interest: Breeding toads or Great Crested Newts, 5 or more submerged, floating or emergent plants or 5 or more dragonflies.
Two	Low wildlife interest: These ponds did not reach the above standards but were not dry or completely overgrown. Duck ponds and those with artificially high numbers of fish are included in this category.
Three	Totally shaded and overgrown by trees
Four	Temporary Ponds: These support specialist invertebrates such as Fairy Shrimp
Five	Dry Ponds: no water at all at the time of survey
Six	Full of rubbish
Seven	New Ponds created since 1985
Eight	Gone without trace
Nine	Not surveyed

Survey Results

The survey forms completed by the volunteers were assessed and put into various grades as demonstrated in Table 2. The parishes were also grouped into 3 categories to show the distribution of the number of ponds per parish.

Table 2: Parish pond survey results in grades

	number of ponds per parish			
	0-4 ponds (18 parishes)	5-10 ponds (21 parishes)	11+ ponds (8 parishes)	total for grade
grade 1	5	27	26	58
2	8	38	24	70
3	2	10	7	19
4	0	3	2	5
5	11	19	6	36
6	3	1	1	5
7	1	11	7	19
8	5	13	9	27
9	11	29	22	62
total for group	46	151	104	301

Ponds with Wildlife Value

It was difficult to divide ponds into a high or low wildlife category (grades 1 and 2) with the limited survey information available. Including such categories also creates the added dilemma of suggesting that the dry, temporary or overgrown ponds do not have any wildlife value which may be untrue. Several ponds in this category were semi -shaded and neglected. Further detailed survey would help to plan suitable management of these ponds in the future.

Overgrown and full of rubbish

Ponds that are heavily shaded by trees with few aquatic plants and stagnant water can look rather unappealing.   However, some shaded ponds especially in old woodland are home to specialized pond invertebrates. There are not many old woodlands in the Cambridge Green Belt Area. Most of the shaded ponds are overgrown by willow trees which can be coppiced or pollarded to reduce shade without removing the tree.

Before the survey began it was thought that many ponds full of rubbish would be found. Only 5 ponds were found to be full of completely full of rubbish which was not in line with expectations.

Dry and Temporary ponds

There were 32 ponds recorded as completely dry. Those in the village centres at Landbeach and Comberton cause particular local concern. Rainfall in 1996 was only 13 inches and this is particularly low . Many ponds were dry in 1996 for the first time ever.

It is difficult to determine the varying effects of low rainfall and lower water tables. Water levels in ponds will vary throughout the year and between years. If a pond dries out in a drought year, many pond animals perish. Occasional drying out is not a disaster and when the pond refills, wildlife is quick to recover. However, there were 3 Great Crested Newt ponds recorded in 1989 but found to be dry in this survey.

The survey recorded 5 temporary ponds which were known from previous surveys to be charactersitic temporary ponds with species such as Fairy Shrimp. The surveyors were not trained to identify invertebrates and perhaps some of the dry ponds could now be called temporary ponds.

New Ponds

There were 22 new ponds created in the Green Belt parishes since 1985. Some of the new ponds are attracting considerable wildlife interest. It is clear that the creation of new ponds has not kept pace with the loss or deterioration of old ones. Five new ponds were created at one golf course. Two new ponds were linked to grant schemes and others were in private grounds or fields. The number of new garden ponds remains unknown, and may well present a brighter future for many of the more common pond plants and animals.

Pond distribution

There is a very uneven distribution of ponds in the Green Belt Area. There were 8 parishes with more than 11 ponds. These 8 parishes also have more than 26 grade one ponds. Four of the eight parishes are grouped together and are a result of coprolite diggings (fossilised dung) in the 18th century. The ponds in this area are now a target for management.

Limitations and advantages of survey method

There was only one survey visit and those early or late in the season limited the available information. Some surveyors were more experienced than others and two people had never looked at ponds before. There were considerable advantages involving local people in gathering information such as landownership and wildlife records outside the survey visit. A Pond booklet was produced and distributed locally, the booklet contained many stories about old ponds collected during the survey. Local publicity also helped to provide a sense of impetus for creating new ponds in gardens and schools. Many volunteers and local people involved in the project were firstly surprised that a temporary pond or a pond covered in vegetation without open clear water might be of high wildlife value. The idea that pond management might be to create a new pond next to the old one or to tackle any clearance over a three year period was also new to many people.

References

Burt G. (1990) A desk survey of the Great Crested Newt in the old county of Cambridgeshire. *Nature in Cambridgehire 32. p59 -63*

Perrin V. & Johnson I. (1995) The Cambridgeshire Dragonfly Survey 1991-1993 *Nature in Cambridgeshire No. 37. p8-19*

Conder A. (1995) Survey of Landscape Change 1994 *Cambridgeshire County Council*

The National Pondlife Centre: An initiative for the new millennium

Andrew Hull

Pond *Life* Project, Liverpool John Moores University, Trueman Building,
15-21 Webster Street, Liverpool, L3 2ET
tel: 0151-231-4044   fax: 0151-258-1224
a.p.hull@livjm.ac.uk

Introduction

A rapidly disappearing, but once common feature in the rural landscape is the pond.   The loss on a vast scale of these small bodies of water, together with the rich diversity of plants and wildlife they support, reinforces the need not only to stimulate awareness and increase understanding of this important rural resource, but also to establish a programme to conserve, protect and manage existing ponds, as well as create new, sustainable pond landscapes.

The proposal to build a *National Pondlife Centre* is based on the belief that there is a pressing requirement for the development of a permanent centre, dedicated to engendering the support and initiating the activity necessary to provide a secure future for Britain's ponds. The centre will carry out research, provide information and, through its dynamic outreach programme, increase awareness and promote further understanding of ponds and the benefit they can provide to the environment, the landscape, wildlife and people.   The *National Pondlife Centre* will be an efficiently managed, non-profit, independent institution, which will provide significant benefit to both the environment and the community at large.   Located in North West England, the *National Pondlife Centre* is planned to be the first phase of a wider development which will see the creation of a number of smaller regional and specialist pondlife centres at strategic locations throughout the United Kingdom

Project Significance

The significance of the *National Pondlife Centre* resides in the following:

- the establishment of a national focus for pond conservation and management, as well as the carrying out of research, and the dissemination of information and outreach to the wider community.
- an opportunity for individuals and educational groups to learn about the ecology of ponds and pond landscapes through visual display and direct experience.
- the promotion of a greater understanding of the importance and value of our ponds and awareness of the continuing threat posed to pondscapes in the United Kingdom and beyond.
- the physical creation of visual representations of the diversity of pondscapes and pond life forms in the United Kingdom and further afield.
- the demonstration of ways in which ponds can be managed for the benefit of the environment, wildlife and the enjoyment of the public.
- acting as a repository for national pond information and relevant biological survey records; and

- becoming an interactive scientific discovery and learning resource centre.

Extension of the project via regional and specialist pondlife centres will strengthen the regional significance of the project and preliminary discussions have been held with a major wetland conservation body already operating at a number of regional sites, as well as a number of other organisations interested in project participation.

Project Benefits

The benefits of the Centre are as follows:

- enhanced nature conservation
- broadened educational opportunities
- opportunity for research and environmental improvement
- improved information base
- effective consultancy
- visitor attraction
- maximising benefits of existing conservation programme
- impact on job creation

The *National Pondlife Centre* will have a number of specific functions including :

- Nature Conservation

The Centre will actively promote pond conservation and establish best practice pond guidelines for use throughout the United Kingdom and beyond. To assist in achieving these objectives, indoor and outdoor exhibition will be created, captive breeding programmes undertaken and a programme of outreach work established. Multi-media and interactive displays as well as walk through aquaria will be developed as a means of gathering greater support for the conservation of ponds and the engendering of awareness of the need for the establishment of responsible management practice.

- Education Opportunities

The broad-based education programme emanating from the Centre will address primary, secondary, tertiary and adult education needs. Where appropriate, these will be developed in line with the requirements of the National Curriculum. A range of training workshops and seminars on pond conservation and management, freshwater ecology and related subjects will be offered both off and on site. The Centre's various educational facilities will be presented in on-site classrooms and laboratory together with the extensive use of existing and newly created ponds on site The development of NVQ and GNVQ courses will be an integral part of the Centre's educational work together with a range of higher level courses which will be accredited allowing access to Higher Education. To support the Centre's on-going educational activities a regular newsletter will be published and the unique 'Adopt-a-Pond' programme will be established and promoted. It is a firm intention that the benefits of the Centre shall be enhanced by a philosophy of outreach especially so in relation to educational (eg. distance learning) and information-base functions.

- Research Opportunities

The provision of research facilities for the advanced study of small freshwater bodies will include the establishment of external field stations associated with the *Regional Pondlife Centres* and *Specialist Pondlife Centres*. Additionally, the on-site research ponds and the development of an overall centre of excellence for the conservation and management of small water bodies will be seen as an important function of the Centre.

- Information Base

The Centre will house the *National Pond Archive* which will include the storage of site biological records relating to ponds throughout the United Kingdom. As part of this outreach programme, emanating from the Centre, the archive will be the location of the *Pond Information Network* (GIS) with on-line access. The archive will incorporate a learning resource centre. Additional activities will include the publication of national and international newsletters, pages on the World Wide Web, contributions to international academic journals, the co-ordination of *Regional Pond Networks* and the organisation of the *Pond Warden Scheme* in North West England and its take-up elsewhere in the United Kingdom (set up as part of the Pond *Life* Project).

- Consultancy:

One of the principal strands of activity to be undertaken by the Centre will be to provide a consultancy service to external bodies, companies and individuals. This will include ecological survey work, the design, creation and restoration of ponds, as well as the development of management programmes. The Centre will operate a comprehensive pond advisory service and on-site demonstration and design facility.

- Visitor Attraction:

The Centre will incorporate an appealing and imaginative visitor attraction. This will enable those visiting the Centre not only to receive information and gain a better understanding of this highly interesting subject, but also the opportunity to experience and enjoy a new and different type of visitor experience. A range of pond types will be constructed, interactive displays and touch pools developed and a walk through aquarium will be established to enable visitors to experience pond life below the surface. It is envisaged that the proposed visitor facilities, when combined with the activities and projects to be carried out by the Centre, will create an attraction of considerable market appeal to a wide potential audience.

The *National Pondlife Centre* capitalises on the expertise generated by the Pond *Life* Project. Emanating from the project are a number of well defined and sustainable outputs which have been trialled in North West England and will be transferred directly to the National Pondlife Centre on completion of the Pond *Life* Project in 1999. In addition to these outputs, the Ponds Research Unit at Liverpool John Moores University will, through the *National Pondlife Centre*, establish an international network - *PondNet* - consisting of academic institutions, research agencies, local authorities and companies as well as nature conservation organisations and agricultural interests. A preliminary network of twelve partners from six countries in the European Union and one from Eastern Europe already exists and will be extended. As part of this initiative, an Internet Web Site will be set up to publicise and promote *PondNet*. A quarterly newsletter will be launched in June 1998 and an international journal is scheduled for 1999.   The editorial office for both of these publications would be at the on opening.

Environmental Impact

As a project with a focus on conservation the energies of the *National Pondlife Centre* are totally committed to environmental improvement.   As far as on-site environmental impact is concerned, the *National Pondlife Centre* will benefit the local environment by creating a visually attractive and ecologically rich pond landscape into which the building is sited.

- The ponds will provide a diverse, accessible and educational pond landscape which will demonstrate the wide variety of pond types that occur, how they can be created, how new ponds can be successfully created and how existing ponds can be restored and managed to provide not only a rich ecological habitat for animals and plants but how they can also provide aesthetic and recreational enjoyment.

- The landscaping surrounding the ponds will be careful selected and designed and will incorporate existing established hedgerows and trees to extend the range of wildlife habitats on the site.

- The ponds and wildlife habitats will form a key element in the ecological and environmental education programme for the Centre. The ponds and landscaping will be designed to be accessible to all visitors including those with disabilities.

The building, both internally and externally, will be designed to the highest architectural standards.   Whilst providing the necessary accommodation to allow the Centre to function properly, the building has been designed to respond to the pond landscape into which it will be located and the edges of what is inside and what is outside has been deliberately blurred. Visitor facilities will include: entrance foyer, exhibition area, UK pond exhibit, Natterjack Toad vivarium, freshwater fish gallery, other ponds (Everglades, Amazon Rainforest), general exhibition areas, discovery and learning resource centre, classrooms, multi-media theatre, general visitor facilities, auditorium, staff and research accommodation, GIS computer suite, and library.

The National Pondlife Centre will be part of a larger agricultural landholding extending to 150 hectares.   This land already contains 30 field ponds and these, together with other landscape features such as hedges, meadow and woodland will be enhanced for the benefit of visitors, educational groups and nature conservation in general.   Additionally, land will also be available for experimental purposes.

The pond warden scheme in north-west England: a preliminary assessment

D.A. Jeffreys and J.S. Rooney

The Pond *Life* Project, Liverpool John Moores University, Trueman Building, 15-21 Webster Street, Liverpool L3 2ET, UK

Introduction

The considerable loss of field ponds in England (Swan & Oldham, 1993) reflects, in part, the world-wide decline of wetland habitats in general. Certainly, within north-west England, the problem of pond loss has been significant. In Lancashire, for instance, 63% of ponds have been lost since 1845 (Grayson, 1994), whilst in Cheshire, 61% of these water features disappeared between the years 1870 and 1993 (Boothby & Hull, 1997).

As a consequence of these, and earlier findings, attempts have been made to safeguard the pond resource. For example, during the 1970s, the Ford Motor Company's 'Save the Village Pond' campaign generated substantial interest by encouraging communities to take an active role in maintaining their local pond (Dyson, 1976). Unfortunately, although such projects attracted considerable initial interest, they lacked the structural support necessary to continue their efforts, and as a consequence proved largely ineffective.

The pond warden scheme

By contrast, the pond warden scheme offers the first sustainable approach to the long term protection of the pondscape. Established first in Cheshire during 1993, and now extended throughout the north-west of England through the European funded Pond *Life* Project, the scheme brings together a network of local volunteers who work within an existing framework of environmental organisations (Boothby *et al.*, 1995).

What sets this scheme apart from its predecessors is the existence of a central organising body, namely the Pond *Life* Project, dedicated to serving the needs of the voluntary warden. This co-ordinating role allows an effective working partnership to be established between volunteers, government and non-government agencies, which ensures the optimum use of time and resources. It should be stated, however, that each organisation plays its own vital role, utilising skills and experiences that enable the project to operate successfully.

The role of the pond warden

The principal actors in the partnership are the pond wardens, whose work is essential. Such volunteers are the local contacts who obtain permission from farmers and landowners to access ponds, and who collect the basic information upon which strategic decisions are made. Their role may simply involve recording the existence of pond sites, which provides invaluable information for updating older source materials. For example, it has been estimated that 35,000 pond sites exist within the north-west of England (Boothby & Hull, 1997). Unfortunately, many of these sites are obscured by trees on the latest aerial photographs, making reliable identification of their status difficult. Ground truthing by pond wardens, therefore, offers an opportunity to accurately assess the number of ponds remaining in the landscape.

Following training workshops, volunteers continue to monitor ponds within their locality, noting species of flora and fauna, together with physical attributes such as water depth and surrounding landuse features. In addition, pond wardens are increasingly utilising the skills of organisations such as the British Trust for Conservation Volunteers (BTCV) in order to undertake pond management and restoration projects of their own.

Pond warden recruitment and distribution

The recruitment of pond wardens has been steady, and to date 175 wardens have been appointed across north-west England (figure 1). A large majority of these volunteers have become wardens out of a general interest in countryside issues, and out of concern for their own local environment. Some have been appointed by parish or town councils, whilst others have been recruited through their involvement with local wildlife trusts.

The task of recruitment falls mainly upon the two pond community officers, who operate within areas north and south of the River Mersey. The principal role of these officers is to raise awareness amongst the general public and to encourage community conservation of the pond environment by forging closer links between farmers, landowners, community groups and schools.

Pond wardens in general take responsibility for their own areas, whether they are rural parishes, or urban towns. A few examine only two or three ponds in areas such as parks or reserves, whereas others monitor several localities. Frequently the duties of the warden are undertaken by one person working alone, but in a number of cases the responsibilities are divided between many individuals in establishments such as schools, conservation groups, angling clubs and ranger services.

Characteristics of volunteers

An interest in conservation issues, and more importantly, a desire to improve the local environment, seem to be the main reasons why volunteers become involved with the pond warden scheme. Such opinions are expressed by all ages, from school children to those in retirement. It is interesting to note that a significantly higher proportion of wardens are male, a fact which perhaps indicates female concern for personal safety when working outdoors.

A brief examination of the employment characteristics of these volunteers has highlighted a range of backgrounds and work experiences, which were found to be fairly constant across the whole of the north west region. A number of individuals were happy to volunteer as a way of making retirement, or time spent at home more varied. Those seeking employment also view the scheme as a way of gaining valuable conservation skills and experiences, qualities which are keenly sought after by potential future employers.

Of those in employment, 20% hold posts which are environmental in nature. Such job titles include, biology teachers, local authority ecologists, wildlife trust officers and countryside rangers. These wardens bring with them extensive knowledge and skills relating to wildlife in

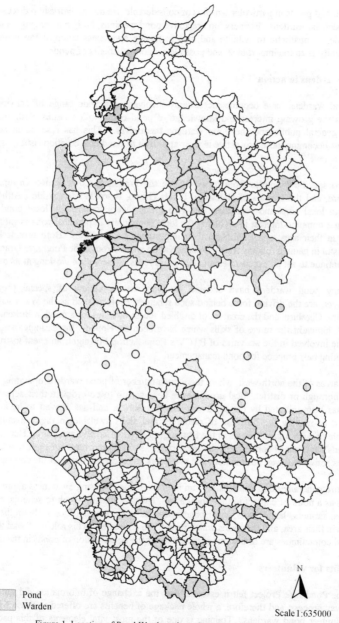

Pond
Warden

Scale 1:635000

N

Figure 1. Location of Pond Wardens throughout North West England.

general, and ponds in particular which is of considerable use during workshop discussions with non-specialist wardens. Farmers too are active pond wardens, both in managing their ponds in a manner sympathetic to wildlife and also in raising awareness amongst the wider farming community as to the importance, and possible economic benefits of ponds.

Pond wardens in action

Pond wardens have become increasingly involved in a wide range of activities, which reflects the growing interest and knowledge of pond conservation issues, both amongst the wider general public and the pond wardens themselves. This has resulted in some pond wardens becoming more pro-active in their approach to pond conservation issues, especially at the local level.

Two specific examples from many include the Frodsham Conservation Group, based in Cheshire, and the Friends of Halewood Ponds Group, based in Merseyside. Although with differing local aims and objectives, the two groups were founded by local pond wardens, sharing a common interest in involving the local community in practical conservation work on ponds in their area, and promoting their importance for wildlife. Both groups have been successful in gaining funding for their conservation work through the Pond *Life* Grant Scheme, and continue to set an excellent example of grass roots conservation working at its best.

Many pond wardens have become involved with a variety of special projects, and moreover, are the driving force behind such schemes. Projects such as the Waterways Trail in Bunbury, Cheshire, and the creation of disabled access facilities for a pond in Birkenhead Park, Wirral, highlight the range of skills which have been developed. Increasingly, wardens have become involved in the activities of BTCV's Pond Action Fortnight, an event instrumental in promoting best practice for pond management.

In areas of the north-west, where there are a number of pond wardens operating within the same borough or district, local groups have been set up to co-ordinate their activities. This idea has been initiated by the pond wardens themselves, and has proved to be an effective method of making the best use of resources and skills available to their advantage. One example of such a group exists in the Borough of Wyre in north Lancashire. Here a group of wardens have joined forces with the local ranger service, and meet up on a regular basis to discuss activities, swap information, and plan work to be carried out over the coming months.

More generally pond wardens play an important role in raising awareness about ponds, by acting as a point of contact in their local area. They continually speak to schools, community groups, farmers, landowners, local businesses and government officers about the status of ponds in their area, and the issues which need to be addressed. This role is of vital importance if local communities are to become responsible for the conservation of ponds in the landscape.

Benefits for volunteers

The Pond *Life* Project felt it essential that the exchange of information did not become a one-way process, and therefore, a whole package of benefits are offered to those who register as volunteer pond wardens. Training is one of the most vital elements of this package, and was one of the first initiatives to be put into practice. Workshops are the start of the training process, with the pond community officers organising five set workshops per year, held across the region. The topics covered include getting started, the identification of amphibians, great crested newts, damselflies and dragonflies, and pond management. Local experts lead these training days, with theory and hands on practical experience.

These workshops have continually proven to be successful, with high levels of attendance being achieved. Many pond wardens have now attended all five workshops, and as a result, new topics are being introduced to increase the scope and level of training available to them. In 1997 new workshops included training in pond invertebrate identification, gaining access and working with landowners, using the Sites of Biological Importance registry, and Natterjack Toad identification.

The culmination of the training workshops is the "Big Splash" conference, where the emphasis is placed upon community involvement. Here new pond wardens have the chance to network with existing ones, and discuss the projects and work that they have been involved with. Held for the first time in 1996, this was an incredibly successful event, which will continue to be an annual focus for the pond warden scheme.

Keeping pond wardens in touch with the project is essential if we are to ensure good communications with all partners and organisations involved. This is carried out mainly through the production of two quarterly newsletters, "Ponds for *Life*" and "Pondscapes". These documents provide an invaluable source of information for pond wardens, updating the latest news and training events, and advising on current funding opportunities. New recruits are introduced, and the additional contributions received by the pond wardens makes these newsletters an interesting and informative read.

One recent benefit has been the introduction of an identification badge for all pond wardens. These cards are useful when visiting farmers and landowners, helping to reassure them of the warden's membership of a recognised conservation project.

Summary

It is hoped that the good-will management of ponds in the landscape can be achieved through community conservation. To this end it is generally accepted that the pond warden scheme is proving to be a successful role model. The principal reason for this has been the way in which volunteers have worked in close partnership with farmers, community groups and environmental organisations. It is this spirit of co-operation which has permitted the gathering of pond data, and enabled practical management tasks to be undertaken throughout the region.

Creating such a scheme has proved worthwhile, although it is not without its problems. The management of the pond warden scheme has clearly demonstrated the need for a dedicated team of staff working full time to co-ordinate the activities of the voluntary wardens. This has proved to be extremely time consuming, although absolutely necessary. Without such staff structures it is easy to see why previous projects failed to maintain their efforts. With correct planning and the appropriate staff in post, there is no reason why the pond warden scheme could not be successfully implemented within other regions. Hopefully, our message of community conservation will be taken up by other willing volunteers who, by conserving their own local pond environment, will help to safeguard the wetland habitats of the world.

References

Boothby, J.; Hull, A.P. & Jeffreys, D.A. (1995) Sustaining a threatened landscape: farmland ponds in Cheshire. *Journal of Environmental Planning and Management*, **38:** (4) 561-568.

Boothby, J. & Hull, A.P. (1997) A census of ponds in Cheshire, north west England. *Aquatic Conservation: Marine and Freshwater Ecosystems*, **7:** 75-79.

Dyson, J. (1976) *The pond book.* Puffin Books, Harmondsworth.

Grayson, R.F. (1994) The distribution and conservation of the ponds of north west England. *Lancashire Wildlife Journal* **2/3:** 23-51.

Swan, M.J.S. & Oldham, R.S. (1993) Pond loss - the present position. C. Alstrop & J. Biggs (Eds). *Proceedings of the Conference: Protecting Britain's Ponds*, Wildfowl and Wetlands Trust/Pond Action, Oxford

Botanical conservation value of East Yorkshire ponds: a comparison of village ponds and clay-pit ponds

S. Linton and R. Goulder

Department of Biological Sciences, University of Hull, Hull HU6 7RX, UK

Introduction

Ponds of diverse origin exist within the landscape of East Yorkshire, North East England. Village ponds and clay-pit ponds have different origins and uses but both have the potential to be of aesthetic and conservation value. Characteristically villages in East Yorkshire had ponds which were used for watering cattle, washing horses and as a water source. In recent years, however, many have been filled in, overgrown or mismanaged. Some of these ponds are marked on old maps as 'The Mere' which implies ancient origin. The clays of East Yorkshire have been extracted for many years leaving behind pits which have sometimes been used for landfill but were often allowed to fill with water. Many have been dug within the last 100 years and may be stocked with fish and used as fishing ponds.

Twelve village ponds and nine clay-pit ponds were studied, and these are referred to here by codes (Table 1). The village ponds are small bodies of water, shallow and ranging in area from 0.004 ha to 0.39 ha. Some almost dry up in the summer months. The clay-pit ponds are generally larger (0.09 ha - 1.61 ha) and deeper. A vegetation survey was made during the summer of 1996 and each pond was allocated a conservation score based on its vegetation. Water chemistry was investigated in the preceding winter.

Methods

The method used for surveying the ponds was a modified version of that used by Pond Action (1993). Emergent and floating-leaved plants were recorded by walking the perimeter of each pond and submerged plants by observation and grapnel hauls. The freshwater macrophyte checklist used was from Palmer and Newbold (1983) with the exception that *Callitriche* was not identified to species. Each pond was surveyed twice, once during May-June 1996 and once during July-August 1996 to ensure early and late flowering species were recorded.

Pond area measurements were taken from the OS 1:2500 scale maps of Humberside kept in the Hull Central Library Local History Department. Some of the ponds had surface areas given on the maps. Otherwise a trace of the pond was made and the area within the paper outline was measured using a Lambda Instruments Corporation (Lincoln, Nebraska) Model LI-3000 Portable Area Meter, and the area in hectares calculated.

A simple method was required to evaluate each pond on the basis of the conservation value of the plants found there. Dony and Denholm (1985) assessed some quantitative methods of scoring woodland sites. One of these used rarity scores; each plant species was assigned a score according to the number of tetrads it occupied within Bedfordshire. Following this idea, a conservation score was calculated for each of the ponds in the present

Table 1. List of ponds studied with National Grid References and area.

Pond name	Code	Grid Reference	Area (ha)
Village ponds			
Great Hatfield	V1	TA 187 431	0.004
Atwick	V2	TA 193 510	0.010
Holme-On-Spalding-Moor	V3	SE 816 388	0.089
Gilberdyke	V4	SE 835 288	0.170
Newland	V5	SE 802 292	0.081
Garton	V6	SE 983 594	0.182
South Dalton	V7	SE 968 454	0.239
Warter	V8	SE 873 505	0.154
Bempton	V9	TA 190 720	0.073
Kilham	V10	TA 066 644	0.077
Bishop Burton (large)	V11	SE 990 398	0.388
Bishop Burton (small)	V12	SE 990 399	0.061
Clay-pit ponds			
Braemar Farm	CP1	TA 214 453	0.500
Fish Ponds Wood 1	CP2	TA 145 675	0.100
Fish Ponds Wood 2	CP3	TA 145 675	0.089
Fish Ponds Wood 3	CP4	TA 145 675	0.278
Fish Ponds Wood 4	CP5	TA 145 675	0.457
Brickyard Farm	CP6	SE 756 427	0.737
Melrose Farm	CP7	SE 762 427	0.360
Hedon	CP8	TA 191 291	1.619
Eastrington	CP9	SE 786 299	0.457

Table 2. Derivation of conservation scores for hydrophytes found in East Yorkshire ponds.

Score	Derivation
6	Aquatic plants recorded from 100 or fewer 10 x 10 km squares in Great Britain and which need special protection in the Yorkshire Water Authority area.
5	Aquatic plants recorded from more than 100 10 x 10 km squares in Great Britain but which need special protection in the Yorkshire Water Authority area.
4	Plants not hitherto recorded or recorded as 'extinct' within East Yorkshire in the *Flora of the East Riding of Yorkshire* (Crackles, 1990).
3	Plants recorded as 'rare' in the *Flora of the East Riding of Yorkshire* (believed to occur in three or fewer localities).
2	Plants recorded as 'uncommon' in the *Flora of the East Riding of Yorkshire* (believed to occur in twelve or fewer localities).
1	Plants recorded as 'infrequent' in the *Flora of the East Riding of Yorkshire*.

study. Scores 6 and 5 were derived from Palmer and Newbold (1983), who considered national conservation value of hydrophytes, and scores 4 - 1 were derived from Crackles (1990) who considered frequency of occurrence of species only in East Yorkshire (Table 2). The scores for the plants recorded at each site were summed to give a total conservation

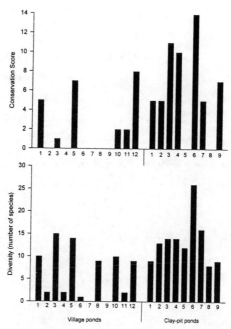

Figure 1. Conservation scores and species diversity for village ponds and clay-pit ponds.

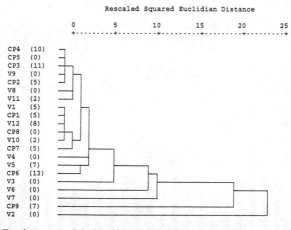

Figure 2. Dendogram produced by hierarchical cluster analysis using the statistical package SPSS for Windows. Input data were standardized results of water analysis. V1 - V12 are village ponds, CP1 - CP9 are clay-pit ponds. Conservation scores for the ponds are shown in brackets.

Table 3. Aquatic macrophyte species recorded for each pond. Conservation scores for individual species are given in brackets.

Aquatic macrophyte species	Village ponds												Clay-pit ponds								
	1	2	3	4	5	6	7	8	9	10	11	12	1	2	3	4	5	6	7	8	9
Acorus calamus (2)	-	-	-	-	-	-	-	-	-	-	+	+	-	-	-	-	-	+	-	-	+
Agrostis stolonifera	-	+	+	-	-	-	-	-	-	+	-	-	-	-	-	-	-	-	-	-	-
Alisma plantago-aquatica	-	-	+	+	+	-	-	-	-	-	+	+	-	+	+	-	+	+	-	-	-
Apium nodiflorum	-	-	-	-	-	-	-	-	-	+	-	-	-	-	-	+	-	-	-	-	-
Berula erecta	-	-	-	-	-	-	-	+	-	-	-	-	-	-	-	-	-	-	-	-	-
Callitriche agg.	+	-	-	-	-	-	-	-	-	-	-	-	-	-	-	-	-	-	-	-	-
Caltha palustris	-	-	-	-	-	-	-	-	-	-	-	+	-	+	+	-	+	-	+	-	+
Carex acutiformis	-	-	-	-	-	-	-	-	-	-	-	-	-	-	-	-	-	-	+	-	+
Carex pseudocyperus (2)	-	-	-	-	-	-	-	-	-	-	-	-	-	-	-	-	-	+	-	-	-
Carex riparia	-	-	-	-	-	-	-	-	-	-	-	-	-	-	-	-	-	-	-	+	-
Ceratophyllum demersum	+	-	-	-	-	-	-	-	-	-	-	-	-	-	-	-	-	-	-	-	-
Crassula helmsii	-	-	-	-	-	-	-	-	-	-	-	-	+	-	-	-	-	-	-	-	-
Eleocharis palustris	+	-	+	-	-	-	-	-	-	-	-	-	-	-	-	-	-	-	+	-	-
Elodea canadensis	+	-	-	-	-	-	-	-	-	-	-	-	-	-	-	-	+	+	-	-	-
Equisetum palustre	-	-	-	-	-	-	-	-	-	-	-	-	-	-	-	-	-	+	-	-	-
Galium palustre	+	-	-	-	-	-	-	-	-	-	-	-	-	-	-	-	-	+	-	-	-
Glyceria fluitans	+	-	-	-	+	-	-	-	-	-	-	-	-	-	-	-	-	-	+	+	-
Glyceria maxima	-	-	-	-	-	-	-	-	-	+	+	+	-	-	-	-	-	-	-	-	-
Groenlandia densa	-	-	-	-	-	-	-	-	-	+	-	-	-	-	-	-	-	-	-	-	-
Hippuris vulgaris	-	-	-	-	-	-	-	-	-	-	-	-	-	-	+	+	+	-	-	-	-
Hydrocotile vulgaris	-	-	-	-	-	-	-	-	-	-	-	-	-	-	+	-	-	+	-	-	+
Iris pseudacorus	+	-	-	-	-	-	-	-	-	-	-	-	+	+	+	+	+	+	+	+	+
Juncus effusus	+	-	+	-	-	-	-	-	-	-	-	-	+	+	+	+	+	-	+	+	+
Lemna minor	+	-	+	-	+	-	-	-	-	-	-	-	+	-	-	-	+	+	+	-	-
Mentha aquatica	-	-	+	-	-	-	-	+	-	+	-	+	+	-	-	-	+	+	-	-	-
Menyanthes trifoliata (1)	-	-	-	-	-	-	-	-	-	-	-	-	-	-	-	-	-	-	-	-	-

168

Myosotis scorpioides

Myriophyllum spicatum

Myriophyllum verticillatum (6)

Nasturtium agg.

Nuphar lutea

Nymphaea alba

Persicaria amphibium

Phalaris arundinacea

Phragmites australis

Potamogeton berchtoldii (2)

Potamogeton crispus

Potamogeton natans

Potamogeton pectinatus

Ranunculus aquatilis (2)

Ranunculus circinatus (5)

Ranunculus flammula

Ranunculus lingua (5)

Ranunculus peltatus (1)

Ranunculus sceleratus

Ranunculus trichophyllus (5)

Scirpus lacustris (3)

Scirpus tabernaemontani (5)

Solanum dulcamara

Sparganium emersum

Sparganium erectum

Typha angustifolia (5)

Typha latifolia

Veronica beccabunga

Veronica catenata

+ denotes presence; - denotes unrecorded.

169

Table 4. Summary of chemical analysis of pond waters.

	Village ponds			Clay-pit ponds		
	Mean	(Range)	CV (%)	Mean	(Range)	CV (%)
PO$_4$-P (μg l^{-1})	169	(<20 - 1062)	190	23.5	(<20 - 54)	90
NH$_4$-N (μg l^{-1})	1558	(44 - 8357)	156	145	(<5 - 444)	92
NO$_2$-N (μg l^{-1})	38.0	(<1 - 259)	193	15.2	(<1 - 63)	130
NO$_3$-N (μg l^{-1})	4847	(<1 - 49136)	289	1054	(66 - 3312)	116
Calcium (mg l^{-1})	57.3	(9 - 150)	90	59.4	(25 - 145)	58
Magnesium (mg l^{-1})	16.3	(2 - 42)	89	29.1	(5 - 88)	103
Sodium (mg l^{-1})	91.5	(28 - 373)	110	95.7	(21 - 347)	115
Potassium (mg l^{-1})	17.0	(<1 - 43)	86	32.1	(<1 - 268)	275
Alkalinity (meq l^{-1})	3.6	(2.2 - 5.6)	26	3.8	(2.8 - 4.9)	19
pH	8.0	(6.7 - 9.2)	7	8.1	(7.6 - 8.5)	3
Conductivity (μS cm^{-1})	928	(383 - 1512)	44	1076	(675 - 3060)	72
Relative turbidity (0 - 100)	9.4	(1.9 - 48)	133	5.7	(2 - 12)	67

score for each pond. If a species fell into more than one category only the higher value was used.

Water samples were collected from all ponds during January-February 1996. On the day of sampling or the following day the water was filtered under vacuum through Whatman GF/C glass microfibre filters. Water samples for ammonium, pH, conductivity and relative turbidity measurement were not filtered. Reactive phosphate was determined using the molybdate method of Mackereth et al. (1978). Ammonium, nitrite and nitrate were determined using the methods of Stainton et al. (1977). Calcium and magnesium were determined by AAS and sodium and potassium by flame photometry. Alkalinity was determined using acid titration (Mackereth et al., 1978). pH and conductivity were measured using appropriate meters and relative turbidity was measured using an Eel Nephelometer (Vogel, 1962).

Results and discussion

Table 3 shows which macrophyte species were recorded for each pond and Figure 1 is a histogram showing species diversity and conservation scores. South Dalton pond (V7) and Bempton pond (V9) contained no macrophytes on the check list. The most diverse pond was Brickyard Farm (CP6) with 26 species; this pond also had the highest conservation score (14). Table 4 summarizes the results of the chemical analysis of the two groups of ponds. Figure 2 is a dendogram produced by hierarchical cluster analysis using the standardized chemical data. This is a statistical analysis which identified clusters of ponds with similar water chemistry.

The clay-pit ponds had significantly higher conservation scores (P < 0.1; Mann-Whitney U-test) and significantly more species (P < 0.05) than the village ponds. The chemical analysis suggested that the village ponds were richer than the clay-pit ponds, with higher concentrations of phosphate, ammonium, nitrite, nitrate and turbidity. The cluster analysis, however, showed that in general each cluster contained both village ponds and clay-pit ponds.

Therefore water chemistry appeared not to closely control conservation score or plant species diversity. Most of the village ponds had large populations of waterfowl, perhaps contributing to the relatively high levels of ammonium. In contrast the clay-pit ponds had only small wildfowl populations, presumably this difference is because ducks are encouraged in village ponds by people feeding them. The clay-pit ponds are mostly managed for angling. The differences in conservation value might be a result of different management regimes; village ponds often undergo sudden, violent disruption as they are periodically dredged to remove silt. In addition they often have concrete or brick margins and are bordered by roads. Thus, there is little margin suitable for colonization and they receive road runoff. The clay-pit ponds are managed more gently; emergent plants are encouraged because an aesthetically pleasing pond is attractive to anglers. Furthermore, anglers trample the margins and often disturb vegetation locally to create more favourable fishing spots. This relatively gentle disturbance might provide a means of burying seeds or propagules to a depth favourable for germination or might stir up buried seed banks.

Acknowledgements

We are grateful for the support of J. Pygott and S. Thorpe of the Environment Agency Leeds; the Environment Agency also provided financial assistance. S. Linton holds a Ferens Schools Scholarship in the University of Hull.

References

Crackles, F.E. (1990) *Flora of the East Riding of Yorkshire*, Hull University Press, Hull.

Dony, J.G. & Denholm, I. (1985) Some quantitative methods of assessing the conservation value of ecologically similar sites. *Journal of Applied Ecology* 22: 229-238.

Mackereth, F.J.H., Heron, J. & Talling, J.F. (1978) *Water Analysis: Some Revised Methods For Limnologists*, Freshwater Biological Association Scientific Publication No. 36, FBA, Ambleside.

Palmer, M. & Newbold, C. (1983) *Wetland and Riparian Plants in Great Britain*, Nature Conservancy Council, Focus on Nature Conservation No. 1, NCC, Shrewsbury.

Pond Action (1993) *National Pond Survey Methods Booklet*, Pond Action, Oxford Brookes University, Oxford.

Stainton, M.P., Capel, M.J. & Armstrong, F.A.J. (1977) *The Chemical Analysis of Fresh Water*, Fisheries and Marine Service Miscellaneous Special Publication No. 25, Fisheries and Environment Canada, Winnipeg.

Vogel, A.I. (1962) *A Textbook of Quantitative Inorganic Analysis*, Third Edition, Longman, London.

An investigation of the ecological and conservation status of wildlife ponds in Sussex.

A. L. Wong and W. A. Young

Chichester Institute of Higher Education, A College of the University of Southampton, Environmental Science Group, Chichester, W.Sussex, UK.

Introduction

This preliminary study aims to survey wildlife ponds in the Sussex area, to compare their ecological and conservation value by focusing on organisms which are indicators of pond stability and health: amphibia, odonata, ephemeroptera, gastropoda and other macroinvertebrates. The long-term objective of this research will be to compare the diversity of artificial wildlife (garden) ponds and natural/semi-natural dew ponds and to identify any trends recorded. Ornamental ponds will be excluded from the study.

Materials and Methods

Ponds surveyed

Three artificial wildlife ponds and one semi-natural wildlife (dew) pond in Sussex were surveyed for amphibians and selected macroinvertebrates between 1992 and 1997. These were between 5 - 20 years' old at the time of sampling, with surface areas of between 12 - 50 m2 and a maximum depth of < 1m and supported a range of macrophytes. Ponds were named according to their site location on the OS map: Brighton, Stanmer Park (Brighton), Charlton (nr. Chichester) and Walberton (nr. Arundel).

Description:

The pond in Brighton has a rockery to the rear and is located in a cemetery garden in an urban setting. The Stanmer Park dew pond is surrounded by shrubs and small trees and is located in deciduous woodland. The Charlton pond is enclosed by fencing to the rear with a rockery and wall to the right-hand side and is located in a residential garden in a semi-rural setting. Walberton pond has a boundary fence to the rear with a rockery and wall to the right-hand side, and is located in a residential garden in a suburban setting.

Sampling techniques

The ponds were surveyed monthly (fortnightly for the Charlton pond) from February to October of 1992 for the two Brighton ponds and from February of 1997 onwards for the two W.Sussex ponds.Three main sampling techniques were used :-

- Visual - for amphibians
- Sweep netting - 10 sweeps across the pond surface and around the edges for invertebrates (eg. snails)
- Silt/detritus collection - a modified aquarium vacuum was used to collect 5 L silt + pondwater in 500ml aliquots taken from different parts of the pond (Wong *et al*, 1994).

Organisms collected using the latter two techniques were sorted into taxa and identified down to species level (Croft, 1986; Clegg, 1986); these were then returned to their respective pond. pH measurements were also recorded for each pond while nitrate and phosphate levels were measured for the Charlton pond .

Results

The survey results are summarised in Tables 1 and 2. Table 1 shows that *Rana temporaria* was recorded for the 4 ponds and was generally present in greater numbers (63 %, 50%, 75% & 67% of the total number of amphibians recorded per pond). *Bufo bufo* was absent from two of the ponds, while *Triturus* sp. were generally least abundant (Table 1). *Triturus cristatus* was not found in any of the ponds surveyed.

Table 2 shows that the most abundant invertebrates were the pulmonate snails (24% & 70%), *Culex* larvae (57%) and *Gammarus pulex* (44%); the least abundant were the dragonfly and damselfly nymphs (2%, 3%, 6% & 2%; Table 2). Mayfly nymphs and caddis fly larvae were not found in the samples collected.

Calculation of diversity

The Shannon-Wiener diversity index , H1 = E (Ni/Ntot x lnNi/Ntot), was applied to the combined data presented in tables 1 and 2 for each pond. The overall H1 value was calculated per pond and were as follows:Brighton = 1.84, Stanmer Park= 1.01,Charlton =1.30, Walberton= 1.28. The Brighton cemetery pond had the highest H1 value while the Stanmer pond had the lowest.

Distribution of indicator species throughout the year

The distribution patterns for amphibians in the four ponds were very similar so the Brighton pond was used as the representative example (Figure 1). It can be seen that *Rana* and *Bufo* numbers peaked in February/March, *Triturus* numbers peaked later on (Figure 1). The distribution of invertebrates in the four ponds followed similar patterns: the snails generally appeared first (Feb/March), then the *Culex* larvae (March), *Gammarus* in March/April and finally the dragonfly/damselfly nymphs in May/June; the Brighton pond was again used as the representative example (Figure 2).

Physico-chemical measurements

The pH recorded for the four ponds was within the range 6.5 - 8.0. The Charlton pond had nitrate levels of 0.0ppm (Feb) - 6ppm (May), and phosphate levels of 10ppm (Feb) to 30ppm (June).

Discussion

Clearly, amphibians and members of the order Odonata use the garden ponds for breeding and were found to be more abundant in these artifical ponds than in the dew pond surveyed. In this study the 'age' of the pond did not appear to be a factor in their use, and this has also been observed for farm ponds (The Open University, 1992). It is interesting to note

Results

Table 1. Maximum number of amphibians recorded per pond.

	Brighton Cemetery	Stanmer Park	Charlton	Walberton
R. temporaria	70 (63.1)	2 (50.0)	6 (75.0)	40 (66.6')
B. bufo	40 (36.0)	2 (50.0)	0 (0.0)	0 (0.0)
T. vulgaris	1 (0.9	0 (0.0)	1 (12.5)	20 (33.3')
T. helveticus	0 (0.0)	0 (0.0)	1 (12.5)	0 (0.0)
Total	**111**	**4**	**8**	**60**

( ): % of the total number of amphibians recorded

Table 2. Maximum number of invertebrates recorded per pond sample by mid-June.

	Brighton cemetery	Stanmer Park	Charlton	Walberton
L. s	19 (21.0)	0 (0.0)	35 (28.5)	100 (69.9)
P.c	22 (24.0)	0 (0.0)	2 (1.6)	40 (28.0)
C.d	0 (0.0)	0 (0.0)	0 (0.0)	0 (0.0)
A.	0 (0.0)	0 (0.0)	0 (0.0)	3 (2.1)
A.p	3 (3.3)	0 (0.0)	0 (0.0)	0 (0.0)
A.s	5 (5.5)	0 (0.0)	0 (0.0)	0 (0.0)
P.	2 (2.2)	0 (0.0)	0 (0.0)	0 (0.0)
C.c	21 (23.1)	20 (57.1)	32 (26.0)	0 (0.0)
T.	0 (0.0)	0 (0.0)	0 (0.0)	0 (0.0)
L.	0 (0.0)	0 (0.0)	0 (0.0)	0 (0.0)
G.p.	19 (20.9)	15 (42.9)	54 (43.9)	0 (0.0)
Total	**91**	**35**	**123**	**143**

( ): % of the total number of invertebrates recorded
Ls: *Limnaeus stagnalis*; Pc: *Planorbis corneus*; Cd: *Cloeon dipterum*; A: *Aeshna* sp; Ap: *Agrion puella*; As: *Agrion splendens*; P: *Pyrrhosoma* sp; Cc: *Culex culex*; T:*Triaenodes* sp; L: *Limnephilus* sp; Gp: *Gammarus pulex*.

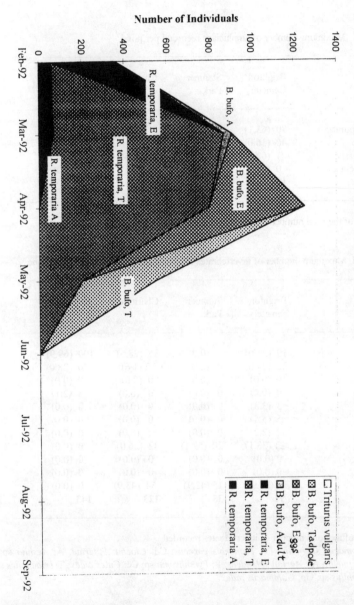

Figure 1. Distribution of Amphibians in Brighton Cemetery Pond (1992)

Number of Individuals

Feb-92 Mar-92 Apr-92 May-92 Jun-92 Jul-92 Aug-92 Sep-92

R. temporaria, E
R. temporaria, T
R. temporaria A
B. bufo, A
B. bufo, E
B. bufo, T

☐ Triturus vulgaris
⊠ B. bufo, Tadpole
⊠ B. bufo, Eggs
⊠ B. bufo, Adult
■ R. temporaria, E
⊠ R. temporaria, T
■ R. temporaria, A

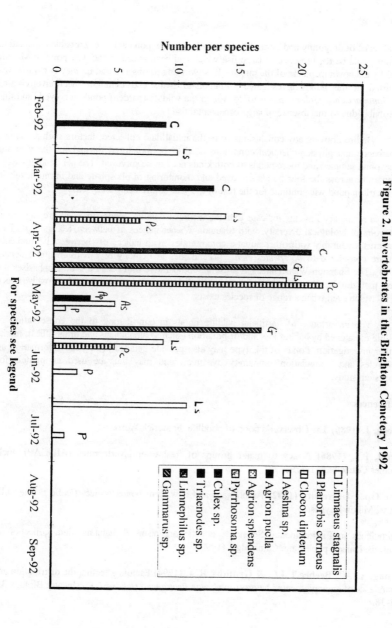

Figure 2. Invertebrates in the Brighton Cemetery 1992

For species see legend

Legend:
☐ Limnaeus stagnalis
⊞ Planorbis corneus
⊟ Clocon dipterum
■ Aeshna sp.
■ Agrion puella
⊠ Agrion splendens
■ Pyrrhosoma sp.
■ Culex sp.
■ Triaenodes sp.
◪ Limnephilus sp.
◩ Gammarus sp.

the absence of dragonfly and damselfly nymphs in the dew pond and the probable explanation for this could be the presence of large fish which had been added to the dew pond in May of 1992 by unknown members of the public. (It is worrying to observe that no mayfly nymph was recorded in the ponds investigated). Pulmonate snails and common macroinvertebrates (eg.*Gammarus* and *Culex*) appear to do well in the wildlife (garden) ponds surveyed and this is probably due to the absence of large ornamental fish !

Before drawing any conclusions from the initial data collected, factors such as human disturbance and physico-chemical conditions need to be monitored throughout the year for every pond sampled and more ponds of both kinds need to be surveyed. The pH readings were comparable across the four ponds surveyed and monitoring of phosphate and nitrate levels in the Charlton pond will continue for the rest of the year before being analysed.

Preliminary findings indicate that the artificial wildlife ponds surveyed are important reservoirs of biological diversity, with Shannon-Wiener indices of between 1.0 and 2.0. This compares favourably with other aquatic communities, with indices of between 1.5 and 3.0, that are considered to be *species rich*. (Techniques in Ecology & Environmental Science, 1990) . The Shannon-Wiener index is a useful, comparative tool because it de-emphasises the effect that 'dominant' species would have on the diversity value - these would normally reduce the H1 value even when a range of species exists.

The importance of artificial wildlife ponds in contributing to the conservation of wildlife threatened by habitat loss and/or pollution (such as amphibians and dragonflies), merits further investigation. Ponds of this type may also provide detailed ecological information on life-cycles and population/community dynamics, and may thus be used as models for ecosystem study.

References

Clegg, J. (1986) The Observer's book of pondlife. Frederick Warne

Croft, P.S. (1986) A key to major groups of freshwater invertebrates (AIDGAP). Field Studies Council : 531-579.

The Open University (1992) Amphibians and new farm ponds project (leaflet). The O.U. Press, Milton Keynes.

Techniques in Environmental Science : aquatic organisms & habitats, data collection & analysis. Daniels publishing, Cambridge. (1990)

Wong, A.L-C; Beebee,T.J.C. & Griffiths, R.A. (1994) Factors affecting the distribution and abundance of an unpigmented heterotrophic alga *Prototheca richardsi*. Freshwater Biology **32**: 33-38.

Notes